Comment on the first ed

MORE
REVEALED

EDITOR
Kathy Espin

MORE REVEALED

Ken Ragge

Foreword and Afterword by Alice Miller

 Alert! Publishing

ALERT!
Published by Alert! Publishing,
P.O. Box 50233, Henderson, NV   89016-0233

To my parents in appreciation for their successful efforts to give me a childhood better than their own and to my many friends who have always stood by me.

CONTENTS

Appendices:

acknowledgments

The people to whom I owe a debt of gratitude for their direct assistance is almost endless but first I would like to thank someone who wasn't directly involved, my college English professor, Margaret Starker. She taught me, in contradiction to everything I already knew, that I had an ability to communicate ideas through writing.

I cannot sufficiently express the gratitude I feel toward friends and family for their encouragement and assistance. Too numerous to mention them all, I would like to single out my sister Claire and brother Ron. They both gave me great encouragement and spent countless hours reading and helping me revise the manuscript. I would also like to thank the many people who read earlier copies of the manuscript and offered criticism and encouragement.

I want to thank Kathy Espin for her kind patience in wielding the editor's knife.

As in any non-fiction work, the ideas expressed are, at the very least, based on the ideas of others. In this respect, I must express gratitude to the people whose names are found in Appendix D. Many of their ideas, although perhaps in a different context, will be found within this text.

PREFACE

The bulk of the sources used in describing AA and its forerunner, the Oxford Group, are from AA and Oxford Group literature. In my analysis of the dynamics of AA I have made every effort to be fair. There is great variation by geographical region in meeting format, readings and language and clichés used. Every effort has been made to stay as close as possible to the original, universal sources of AA doctrine; the official literature, most particularly the "Big Book" and "Twelve Steps and Twelve Traditions."

Since this is not a scientific work *per se*, usually only one study, and at most two, are used to back up a point. Other sources of documentation, and more thorough works on the various areas of the text, are listed in Appendix D. The ones cited here are generally the most methodologically sound, the first, and/or the most frequently cited.

In the chapter "What is addiction?," although the word "definition" is used, the attempt is to be expository rather than definitive.

In some of the sections on the origin of addictions, few sources are listed. The models used are purely for the context of addiction, and therefore no distinction is made between, for example, over-learned behavior and other learning, and between emotions and feelings. While the distinctions in language are extremely important in the laboratory, "a sense of self-efficacy" translates much better to the rest of us as "self-confidence" or a "can do attitude." Hopefully, an easily understandable and enlightening view of addiction has been presented.

The Twelve Steps

Step One: We admitted we were powerless over alcohol—that our lives had become unmanageable.

Step Two: Came to believe that a Power greater than ourselves could restore us to sanity.

Step Three: Made a decision to turn our will and our lives over to the care of God as we understood God.

Step Four: Made a searching and fearless moral inventory of ourselves.

Step Five: Admitted to God, to ourselves, and to another human being the exact nature of our wrongs.

Step Six: Were entirely ready to have God remove all these defects of character.

Step Seven: Humbly asked Him to remove our shortcomings

Step Eight: Made a list of all persons we had harmed, and became willing to make amends to them all.

Step Nine: Made direct amends to such people wherever possible, except when to do so would injure them or others.

Step Ten: Continued to take personal inventory and when we were wrong promptly admitted it.

Step Eleven: Sought through prayer and meditation to improve our conscious contact with God as we understood Him, praying only for knowledge of His will for us and the power to carry that out.

Step Twelve: Having had a spiritual awakening as the result of these steps, we tried to carry this message to alcoholics, and to practice these principles in all our affairs.

Foreword

Ken Ragge's book will be a shock to many people because it reveals facts they would rather not know. But the shock, I have no doubt, will be a healthy one. Facing facts and giving up illusions can be extremely painful but, in the long run, it is always healthy. In contrast to depression, this pain has a start and an end. Whether or not a person is ready to go through this process of grieving yet does not depend only on a book, of course, but on his own situation. The right information given at the right time can be life-saving. The same information given at the wrong time will be without effect. It will have to wait. I sometimes get letters saying: "I bought your book some years ago because it was recommended to me, but I thought it rather boring and stopped reading after a few pages. Last night, however, I read it through and I felt that you must have written it just for me..."

More Revealed is an offer, an invitation. It is an invitation to open your eyes, to look around, to verify information, to ask questions, to refuse to be fooled, and to slowly become aware of the prison of illusions that suffocates your life. Unlike indoctrination and brainwashing, an invitation gives you full freedom to accept it or not. You can even postpone your decision for months or years. But once you decide to accept the invitation, to leave the prison and to face facts, you have made a new discovery, the discovery of freedom. And in the light of this discovery the wall of illusions bound tightly to obedience crumbles, giving space to your real, never-before-experienced life.

Alice Miller
September, 1992

Chapter 1

In the Beginning...

"The worst of madmen is a saint run mad."
– Pope[1]

In 1939, shortly after its founding, Alcoholics Anonymous was in debt and its membership broke. Hope for the organization's financial stability was pinned to the sale of their newly-published book; "Alcoholics Anonymous." A small group of early AA members, including cofounder Bill Wilson, were discussing what to do. Morgan, a new member, had an idea. He had connections in the media from his days as an advertising man. He could arrange for an interview on a popular nationwide radio program. As the AA literature tells it,

"[S]omebody sounded a note of caution: What if the lately released asylum inmate Morgan should be drunk the day of the broadcast! Hard experience told us this was a real possibility. How could such a calamity be averted?

Very gently we suggested to a resentful Morgan that he would have to be locked up somewhere until the night of the broadcast. It took all of salesman Henry's wiles to put this one over, but he did. How and where we would lock him up was the only remaining question. Henry, with full faith now restored, solemnly declared that 'God would provide.' ...Grumbling loudly, Morgan was conducted into captivity. For several days we took turns staying with him right around the clock, never letting him get out of our sight....

Sighs of relief went up in every New York member's home when Morgan's voice was heard. He had hit the deadline without getting drunk. It was a heart-stirring three minutes."[2]

Morgan told a tale of alcoholic ruin and the recovery he and others had found in AA.[3]

What went on there? The group was so afraid Morgan would go on a binge, they locked him up so he could go on the air to tell how they helped him recover from his drinking problem. If hard experience told them he was likely to get drunk, how good was his "recovery"? If they didn't have faith in his sobriety, how much faith did they have in their program?

To understand their behavior it is first necessary to have some knowledge of the history of Alcoholics Anonymous and the workings of its parent, the Oxford Group.

The AA story begins with Frank Buchman, a Lutheran minister from Pennsylvania. In China in 1918, he began holding a series of meetings called "house parties." A house party was defined as, "...an informal gathering of friends in a hotel or college ...where countless people who would never have darkened the door of a church

4

found a practical, working faith in surroundings where they felt at home."[4] Buchman was attempting to bring about a revival of what he perceived to be first-century Christianity, hence his group's first name: "First Century Christian Fellowship." While Buchman and his loose knit "fellowship" made much of non-existent ties to internationally prestigious Oxford University, the name "Oxford Group" was reportedly coined by a South African baggage handler in 1921.[5]

world peace through "God-control"

Literature from the 1930s, when AA and Oxford Group were one, describes their major goals. From one of leader Frank Buchman's speeches,

> "...The secret is God-control. The only sane people in an insane world are those controlled by God. God-controlled personalities make God-controlled nationalities. This is the aim of the Oxford Group.
>
> The true patriot gives his life to bring his nation under God's control. Those who oppose that control are public enemies. ...
>
> World peace will only come through nations which have achieved God-control. And everybody can listen to God. You can. I can. Everybody can have a part."[6]

Oxford Group was the bearer of the secret of sanity. Members, being sane people, had the power to make others sane. This was the "patriotic" duty to which members were to dedicate their lives. All who opposed their plans for "world peace" (Oxford Group world domination) were public enemies. Everyone was welcome to join in the great, moral crusade.

For those who were *too insane* to join on their own, Oxford Group had special methods to help them called "the five C's." Once "helped" with the five C's, one could live life sanely, meaning in accordance with "the five procedures" and "the four absolutes."

the four absolutes: the yardstick of sanity

The four absolutes are absolute purity (which refers predominately to sex), absolute honesty, absolute unselfishness and absolute love. The absolutes were the measuring sticks by which one's actions and thoughts were to be judged. At first glance, they seem to be a worthy ideal. Use of the absolutes, however, could hardly have served other than to make the Oxford Groupers feel absolute guilt or in absolute contempt of their God-given reasoning ability.

To understand this, imagine a man with only one dollar in his pocket. He is waiting for the bus to work. The fare is exactly one dollar. An obviously poorly fed pan-handler asks for some change for food. To be absolutely unselfish, the man would have to give up the dollar. But what about his obligation to his employer and his family? Would it be absolutely loving to miss work and possibly lose his job and not be able to provide for his family? But isn't it a violation of absolute unselfishness to be concerned only with his family? The pan-handler is so obviously in need.

In terms of the absolutes, there is no rational, logical,

guilt-free solution. One's ability to reason is worthless, as there is no "spiritual" solution through logic. Any logical solution would leave the man a guilty sinner. He would be doomed to fall short of the ideal.

This seemingly lose-lose situation presented no problem for groupers. They held the intellect in scorn anyway, probably as a direct result of the absolutes. In their belief system, people were stymied in their spiritual growth to the degree they ran their lives by their own will. Humans were obviously unable to run their own lives anyway.

Reason suspended, the groupers had a "spiritual" way of dealing with all of life's problems, no matter how huge or trivial. Groupers had Guidance.

the five procedures of the sane

The first of the five procedures, Guidance, was to listen for messages from God. Members were to spend an hour in the morning in meditation, pen in hand, and write all thoughts that came to mind. The next procedure, checking guidance, was to determine whether the thoughts were from the sub-conscious, from the evil one, or from God Himself. They were first checked against the four absolutes. They were then checked by other group members.* Elders were particularly important in

---

*This is a common device for religious cults of all types. The member is told to ask for "Divine Guidance," and then to subject it to other members' interpretation. Imagine if a member believed that God had told him that the doctrine was wrong in some respect, or perhaps even that the sect was evil and he should leave. The group, of course, would make every effort to help him to understand that he was

7

this because they were further along the Spiritual Path and therefore better able to determine what was really from God.

Guidance was also considered available all through the day. Not only was Guidance relied upon to know what to do if a problem should arise but also to determine what a member should do with his time or what to prepare for dinner[7]. The procedure of "giving in to God," complete "surrender" to Guidance, was complete surrender to God. Surrender to God was God-control. It was sanity.

Another procedure was Restitution. Amends were to be made for past shortcomings. These shortcomings were predominately the sins committed before having "surrendered to God," or "giving in to God," as measured against the four absolutes.

The fifth procedure, "sharing," was made up of two parts: sharing for witness and sharing for confession. Sharing for witness was also known as "The Fifth Gospel" and "The Gospel of Personal Experience." These names are particularly appropriate because Oxford Group considered sharing for witness the equivalent of the New Testament gospels.[8] In other words, an elder grouper's sermon was considered as wise, true and as spiritually inspired as the words of Matthew, Mark, Luke and John.

Sharing for confession was the confession of sins. Unlike most Christian churches, this wasn't done between oneself and God, with a priest in private or, to a limited extent, at a service. Open confession, along with

---

mistaken. It wasn't God. It was Satan, or whatever evil force the particular cult used to maintain obedience, suggesting such things.

"sharing for witness," were the central core of the meeting experience.

Oxford Group's meetings were rather informal. Everyone was on a first-name basis. They had no "clerical class," relying instead on the elders as preachers. The preacher, or leader, was any elder who was thought to have a particularly relevant "message" or "story" for that evening. For instance, if a newcomer was expected to be present, someone with a similar background or who suffered from similar sins prior to being saved might be chosen by the members to lead.

After the reading of selected Bible passages, the leader would speak first. His sharing would begin with the confession of sins of the past and end with the rewards of "surrender" to God-control through the Oxford Group. After the sermon, members would give confession and witness from the floor. The meetings were described as both extremely emotional and hypnotic and there was often a great deal of good-natured laughter.

the five C's

The most important duty of Oxford Group members was to win souls for Christ. Since most targets for recruitment were already members of Christian churches, it is more accurate to say they worked to win souls for the Oxford Group. The five C's were the "scientific" method of "life-changing," or making the insane sane, presented in an Oxford Group manual called "Soul Surgery[9]." The five C's are Confidence, Confession, Conviction, Conversion and Conservation.[10]

Non-groupers, in spite of being members of Christian

churches, were characterized as "hungry sheep who are dependent upon us, whether or not they or we realize it, for finding the way to the great spiritual Shepherd of men's souls."[11] In order to find the target of scientific conversion, Guidance was used. After "God" told them who to go after, the grouper would "lay siege with all the powers, seen and unseen, that he can muster to his support."[12]

The first step in working with others, or "laying siege," was to come "so wholly into the confidence of the one we seek to help along the avenue of personal friendship that we know his verdict on his own case, see him through his own eyes."[13]

In winning the confidence of the "lost sheep," the grouper is advised to "avoid argument" and "[a]dapt the truth to the hearer's need."[14] While "adapting the truth" might seem to fall short on the yardstick of Absolute Honesty it must be remembered that, having adopted the absolutes, the grouper's reason is suspended and the inconsistency could not be noticed. It also would be unreasonable to expect a sane person (a person under God-control) to question the morality of any action necessary to make the insane (those not under God-control) sane. After all, he is following direct orders from God as communicated through Guidance. It is easy to imagine that in the grouper's mind he must have seen himself as "serving Higher Purpose."

The second C, Confession, was used as a means of manipulation. Whereas in Christianity, as in other major religions, confession is a method of clearing the conscience, of removing a sense of separateness from God, in the Oxford Group, as in other cults, confession ultimately served quite different purposes.

> "Through the avenue of confidence we win a man's friendship. Through confession we may win his soul..."[15]

> "[I]f we are honest and humble and truthful, God will keep us human and sympathetic, and may be able to use our very weaknesses and temptations..."[16]

Honesty, humility and truth are, of course, admirable qualities. However, it is somewhat less than absolute honesty to feign friendship and, with ulterior motives and absolutely devoid of real penitence, go through the act of confession. It is also arrogant to assume that anyone who isn't a fellow Grouper is a lost sheep who needs to be "helped."

Confession had another use for the Oxford Group soul surgeon:

> "To go with a confession of unworthiness...tends to disarm criticism..."[17]

The second C, the extraction of Confession, was considered of ultimate importance and great effort was made to get it.

> "When he is certain that the need for confession exists, the soul surgeon must be lovingly relentless in insisting that the confession be made..."[18]

This "loving relentlessness" takes on a rather sinister air when the group's "hospital work" is considered. An alcoholic patient, locked away in a hospital, would be given only a Bible to read and was allowed only Groupers for visitors during the "Oxfordizing" period.* The poor victim was under steady pressure, perhaps for days, weeks or months, to accept Oxford Group interpretations of the Bible and Oxford Group's will as God's will. Even outside of hospitals, the grouper's techniques sometimes led to severe emotional damage including nervous and mental breakdowns.[19]

The third of the five C's, Conviction, was defined as "a vision of the hideousness of his own personal guilt..."[20] If the lost sheep didn't seem to feel guilt intensely enough, effort was made to increase and intensify it.[21]

Sincere confession, confession for what one feels a genuine sense of guilt and shame, was used by the Oxford Group member, as in other cults, for further manipulation. Having "befriended" the lost sheep, gotten a confession of guilt and intensified that guilt, the grouper now had the lost sinner in an extremely vulnerable position. The lost sheep, overwhelmed by *the hideousness of his own personal guilt*," needed resolution. His grouper "friend" had already prepared a way out. The soul surgeon had already described, in *humble* confession, how he was saved by "the programme of His Kingdom."

The lost sheep was almost found. All he needed for Conversion, the fourth C, was to have faith. This meant to be *obedient* to "the programme of His Kingdom" since faith, for the Oxford Group, was defined as obedience.[22]

For the soul surgeon, the work is not yet done. One

---

*All cults use some method to separate their target from outside sources of information.

final C, Continuance, remains. The most important element in Continuance was to get the new convert working at converting others. The convert is told, "[A]s we have freely received, so we must freely give." This was because it was "...one of the surest safeguards against its [the conversion experience] soon becoming unreal."[23] *In order for a grouper to maintain his unusual beliefs he had to convince others of their truth.*

The degree to which one's life is changed by this process is great. "The central pivot around which his life revolves must now be not self but others, not serving his own interests or development but serving and winning others..."[24] Anything interfering with full dedication to "winning others" would be considered selfish at best. Some of the reasons given for weak dedication to practicing soul surgery were spiritual laziness, spiritual cowardice and "Satan's active interference."[25] Needless to say, believing this would intensify a slacker's feelings of guilt, leading to an even greater dependence on Guidance and need to win converts.*

The Oxford Group was most concerned with bringing rich, famous and powerful public figures under God-control so their influence could be used to sway the public. One apparent success, the son of rubber baron Harvey Firestone, was to play an important part in the birth of Alcoholics Anonymous and have a great influence on its development.

---

*Robert J. Lifton, the world's foremost authority on "totalitarian organizations," refers to the psychological need of the converted to convert others as "the psychology of the pawn."

"...events were taking place independently in two American cities which were to lead to his [Buchman's] principles being applied to such hospital cases by [Alcoholics Anonymous], first throughout America and then all over the world.

In Akron, Ohio, Jim Newton...found that one of Firestone's sons was a serious alcoholic. He...took him first to a drying-out clinic...and then on to an Oxford Group conference in Denver. The young man gave his life to God, and thereafter enjoyed extended periods of sobriety. The family doctor called it a 'medical miracle'.

Firestone Senior was so grateful that, in January 1933, he invited Buchman and a team of sixty to conduct a ten-day campaign in Akron. They left behind them a strong functioning group which met each week in the house of T. Henry Williams...Among them were an Akron surgeon, Bob Smith, and his wife Anne. Bob was a secret drinker..."[26]

Dr. Bob Smith was to become revered as one of the two co-founders of Alcoholics Anonymous.

The Oxford Group, through the Firestone publicity, presented itself as having a "program" explicitly for drunks in addition to sinners in general. The meeting left behind at T. Henry Williams' in 1933 was an Oxford Group meeting and was to stay that way for several more years.

Meanwhile, in New York, the other co-founder-to-be was on a downhill slide with his drinking problem. Bill Wilson was first hospitalized at Towns Hospital in New York City. During his first two stays, his doctor, William Silkworth, impressed on him the hopelessness of alcoholism. Silkworth's theory on alcoholism was that it was "an allergy combined with a mental obsession," and that abstinence was the only remedy. Once a drink was taken, the allergy would take over and an "alcoholic" could not stop.

Armed with the knowledge that he was "Powerless over alcohol and that just one drink would cause him to lose control," Wilson's condition got decidedly worse. While previously he might go months without a drinking binge, after "treatment," Wilson would "work through hangover after hangover, only to last four or five days, or maybe one or two."[27]

Wilson, perhaps with direct coaching from Silkworth, came to the conclusion that "...nothing could keep him from what he would later call the 'insidious insanity' of taking the first drink."[28]

His mental state became so bad after "treatment" that "Terror, self-hatred, and suicidal thoughts became his constant companions. ...[H]e contemplated suicide—by poison, by jumping out the window."[29]

Meanwhile, unknown to Wilson, an old drinking buddy he hadn't seen in five years was getting a message directly from God. In Guidance with other groupers, "God" told Wilson's friend, Ebby, to visit him. Ebby's visit was in November 1934.

They talked for several hours. One of the things that impressed Wilson most during the visit was that "Ebby looked different; there was a new way about him..."[30] When asked what happened, Ebby answered, "I've got religion."[31] Wilson was also impressed that Ebby didn't preach. As noted previously, in Oxford Group conversion techniques the method wasn't to preach but to first confess to win confidence. Apparently this is what Ebby did. To quote AA literature, "Ebby had told his story simply, without hint of evangelism."[32]   An integral part of his story was salvation from drinking by the Oxford Group, which he described as more spiritual than religious.

During the ensuing days, Wilson remained impressed with the fact that while he was drinking, Ebby was sober.* This led Wilson to set out for Calvary Mission where the Oxford Group held meetings. Wilson arrived drunk.

At its American headquarters, the Oxford Group dealt particularly with drunks. As Wilson later described it,

> "...the derelict audience. I could smell sweat and alcohol. What the suffering was, I pretty well knew."

and continued,

> "Penitents started marching forward to the rail. Unaccountably impelled, I started, too... Soon, I knelt among the sweating, stinking penitents. ...Afterward, Ebby...told me with relief that I had done all right and had given my life to God.[33]"

After the meeting, Wilson was told to go to Towns Hospital where Ebby and other group members could see him. Two or three days later, Wilson checked in.

At Towns, he was given the standard treatment, barbiturates and several hallucinogens, including bella-

---

*Ebby later died from drinking. see Pittman (1988):157

donna and henbane, until "the face becomes flushed, the throat dry, and the pupils of the eyes dilated."[34]

After several days, Ebby came to see him. While there is no record of what was said, it is recorded that after Ebby left, "Bill [Wilson] slid into a very deep melancholy. He was filled with guilt and remorse over the way he had treated Lois [his wife]..."[35] Evidently, Ebby had done something to provoke it and, knowing the five C's, it is easy to put together what happened.

Ebby was sent to Wilson in a Guidance session. He won Wilson's "Confidence" through "humble confession," eliciting a confession from Wilson. Apparently, Wilson confessed to something he had tremendous guilt over; the way he had treated Lois. Ebby was able to use this to give Wilson a "vision of the hideousness of his own personal guilt."

Now the time of Conversion was upon Wilson. In what appears to have been a drug-and-stress-induced hallucinatory breakdown, Wilson found "the programme of His Kingdom." From that day forward, Bill Wilson never drank again.

By 1935, Wilson and his wife were both regular attendees at Oxford Group meetings. He was very impressed with what he saw and heard. As he described it,

> "On the platform and off, men and women, old and young, told how their lives had been transformed. ...Little was heard of theology, but we heard plenty of [the absolutes]... Confession, restitution, and direct guidance of God underlined every conversation. They were talking about morality

and spirituality, about God-centeredness versus self-centeredness."[36]

Knowing that, "If he did not work, he would surely drink again, and if he drank, he would surely die,"[37] Wilson set out to "work with others." This was the fifth C, Continuance. Rather than go to work to support himself and his wife, over whom he had felt such guilt, he dedicated himself, full-time, with a "burning confidence and enthusiasm," to "give freely that which was so freely given."

After six months Wilson was a total failure, not having saved one drunk. The groupers were reportedly "cool" to his "drunk-fixing." Whether they were upset because of his failure or because he concentrated only on drunks is not clear.*

Part of Wilson's "vision" was to create a "chain" of alcoholics; one bringing others who brought others under God-control. Oxford Group was after everyone, not just drunks. Independent of AA literature, a writer on Frank Buchman's life quotes someone telling Wilson, "You're preaching at these fellows, Bill. No one ever preached at you. Turn your strategy round."[38]

This seems to indicate that Wilson's early problem with the Oxford Group's coolness towards him was more a matter of incompetence at "soul surgery."

In mid-1935, Dr. Silkworth came to Wilson's rescue. He gave Wilson some advice that was to have a profound

---

*It is interesting to note that while at this time he was, according to AA literature, under criticism for being concerned exclusively with drunks, he would be later described in the Big Book (Alcoholics Anonymous) as planning to save the entire world.

impact and lead Wilson to great success winning souls in a different fashion. It also was to lead, over the next few years, to schism from the Oxford Group for him and his soon-to-be-gathered flock of lost sheep.

Silkworth advised him to not talk about the absolutes and his spiritual (conversion) experience at first with potential converts. He was told,

> "You've got to deflate these people first. So give them the medical business, and give it to them hard. Pour it right into them about the obsession that condemns them to drink and the physical sensitivity...that condemns them to go mad or die... Coming from another alcoholic...maybe that will crack those tough egos deep down. Only then can you begin to try out your other medicine, the ethical principles you have picked up from the Oxford Groups."[39]

This advice, to use fear to make indoctrinees amenable to conversion through guilt, was new to the Oxford Group. It wasn't long before Wilson had the opportunity to try out the new techniques, but first, one more missing piece was to be put in place.

In May 1935, Wilson made a business trip to Akron, Ohio. Alone in a strange city, he was tempted to enter a bar. He was afraid he would drink. He realized he needed a drunk to work on. Although he hadn't yet saved anyone, trying to seemed to have kept him from drinking. It was at this point he realized what is considered by present-day groupers to be a milestone in the birth of AA, that, "You need another alcoholic just as much as he needs you!"[40]

Armed with the knowledge that "working with another" would be protection from drinking and the inevitable insanity or death of alcoholism, he set out to find his subject. After contacting an Akron grouper, he was put in touch with Dr. Bob Smith, the "secret" drinker in T. Williams' group. Smith had been a grouper for years but had admitted his drinking problem just weeks before Wilson's arrival. AA literature describes the encounter:

> "'[I (Wilson)] went very slowly on the fireworks of religious experience.' First, he talked about his own case until Bob 'got a good identification with me.' Then, as Dr. William D. Silkworth had urged, Bill hammered home the physical aspects of the disease, 'the verdict of inevitable annihilation.'"[41]

Smith, after one more drinking spree, stopped drinking permanently. Bill Wilson and Dr. Bob were soon at work bringing new souls into the Oxford Group and under God-control. Before Wilson returned to New York, they had formed "that first frightened little group of Akron alcoholics, each wondering who might slip next."[42]

While this "frightened little group" held beliefs almost identical to the Oxford Group, the difference which would lead inevitably to schism already existed. It was the difference in conversion techniques. Oxford Group soul surgery techniques called for augmentation of guilt leading to the conversion experience. The alcoholics had learned, through their own conversion, a different method; augmentation of fear with an *initial* diminution of guilt. "It's not you're fault, it's a disease. There is nothing you can do about it. You'll die unless you believe."

When a person was properly convinced and reached a

point of proper desperation, guilt was then applied to bring about conversion to God-control. These new groupers were motivated, not primarily by guilt, but by fear.

Other groupers, being God-controlled through guilt, were accustomed to using guilt to manipulate others. This evidently irritated the growing number of alcoholics in Oxford Group. Wilson attributed this friction to the particular nature of alcoholics,

> "[D]rinkers would not take pressure in any form, excepting from John Barleycorn himself. They always had to be led, not pushed. ...When first contacted, most alcoholics just wanted to find sobriety, nothing else. ...They simply did not want to get 'too good too soon.'" [43]

This indicates the early genesis of AA's belief in the uniqueness of alcoholics and also the need for a new, slower conversion process to complete God-control.

Another cause of irritation on both sides was that the alcoholics' sins were so much worse than those of many of the other groupers. One of the early alcoholics in the Oxford Group, responding to a non-alcoholic grouper saying that smoking was his worst sin, thought "Oh yeah? Well, that pipe will never take you to the gutter."[44]

While alcoholic groupers took pride in their sins and scorned the trivialness of the sins of the non-alcoholic groupers, the non-alcoholics saw the alcoholics as lowering their prestige.[45]

The Oxford Group in New York apparently wasn't as tolerant of the fear-converted alcoholics as the group in Akron. Wilson, who had formed a group in the fall of

1935, was soon to learn that the Calvary Mission groupers were told not to go to his meeting. According to AA literature, it was thought that Wilson's group was not "maximum,"[46] meaning they were less than totally dedicated. Wilson's guidance was considered off.[47] He didn't give all the credit to Oxford Group.[48] (Perhaps that is how they knew his guidance was off.) The alcoholics limited themselves to saving other alcoholics.[49] Another major issue was that the alcoholics preferred to remain anonymous which was contrary to Oxford Group methods of public witness. Rather than breaking away from Oxford Group, as Wilson's wife Lois described it, the Oxford Group "kind of kicked us out."[50] New York AA was on its own in 1937.

In 1938, Wilson set to work writing the Big Book, a sacred text for all alcoholics. The purposes of the book were to "[set] forth a clear statement of the recovery program," "prevent distortion of the message," "publicize the movement," and, hopefully, "make money."[51]

It was in the writing of the Big Book that the core of AA's "program of recovery" was first formalized as "The Twelve Steps." While the first and last step mentioned alcohol, they were, for all other practical purposes, the Oxford Group *"programme."* AA literature describes the writing of the Steps,

> "As he started to write, he asked for guidance. And he relaxed. The words began tumbling out with astonishing speed. He completed the first draft in about half an hour, then kept on writing until he felt he should stop and review what he had written. Numbering the new steps, he found that they added up to twelve — a symbolic number; he thought of the Twelve Apostles, and soon became convinced

that the Society should have twelve steps."[52]

To this day, when an AA member is questioned about the origin of the steps, the response will probably include the phrase "spiritually inspired," meaning that they came directly from God to Bill Wilson's pen. Of course, being "spiritually inspired," The Twelve Steps are beyond reproach.

The first edition of the Big Book was published in April 1939.[53] It contributed to the break with the Oxford Group in Ohio where there were problems keeping alcoholic Catholics in the Akron group. The Oxford Group used the King James version of the Bible and engaged in open confession. Both practices clashed with Catholic teaching.[54]

It was a difficult situation since the alcoholics felt they owed their lives to Oxford Group. Some members decided, presumably with God's Guidance, to start their own separate meeting in Cleveland. Free from Oxford Group control, they could obey God.

Apparently, one of His earliest instructions was to throw out the Bible. The Big Book could be used at meetings instead. The book had been carefully worded to avoid offending Catholics. They could now describe themselves as spiritual (they were concerned with "fitting themselves into God's plan"), not religious (they didn't use the Bible as their ultimate authority). Being "spiritual, not religious," confession didn't exist. It was sharing. The Cleveland group was the first to report the effectiveness of the Big Book in converting hospitalized patients.[55]

The Bible was found to be unnecessary, *irrelevant*. It

is interesting to note that Oxford Group's "Fifth Gospel" put personal testimony *on a par with* the New Testament. Alcoholics Anonymous, at their founding, put it *above* the Bible.

In the latter part of the 30s, it became important to AA to disassociate itself, at least in the public eye, from the Oxford Group because of the growing distrust and contempt the American public held for the Group. In August 1936, Frank Buchman was quoted by a major New York newspaper,

> "I thank heaven for a man like Adolf Hitler, who built a front line of defense against the anti-Christ of Communism....Of course, I don't condone everything the Nazis do. Anti-Semitism? Bad, naturally. I suppose Hitler sees a Karl Marx in every Jew. But think what it would mean if Hitler surrendered to the control of God. ...The world needs a dictatorship of the living spirit of God. ...Human problems aren't economic. They're moral, and they can't be solved by immoral measures. They could be solved within a God-controlled democracy, or perhaps I should say a theocracy, and they could be solved through a God-control-led Fascist dictatorship."[56] *

---

*In "The Open Secret of MRA," a defense of Buchman and Buchmanism, the complete text of the New York World-Telegram article is included. It is interesting to note the differences in the original from 1936 and AA's abbreviated version published in 1984 on pages 170-171 of Pass It On. AA quoted in a fashion that put Buchman in a much better light than even the Buchmanites had attempted to. Most of what is quoted here was left out of the AA version. Perhaps most interesting is that, in the AA version, "the control of" is dropped out of mid-sentence, changing "surrender to the control of God" to "surrender to God." Apparently, Oxford Group language was still considered too hot to print in AA literature, even when quoting Oxford

These and other charges of Nazi sympathies,* didn't sit well with the American people. Frank Buchman and his organization's Guidance were in serious question.

Buchman's statements served notice on the American people how misguided and dangerous it can be to believe one's thoughts are the Word of God.

Though they pale against the charges of Nazi sympathies, other criticisms were leveled against the Oxford Group. Most involved arrogance due to Oxford Group's belief that they alone were sane and getting direct messages from God and that others, even members of Christian churches, were lost sheep. These charges included blindness to thinking, undercutting churches, hypocracy, self-congratulatory sanctimoniousness and an inability to tolerate criticism.

Just as Oxford Group hit its crest of popularity, public awareness hit its zenith causing their popularity to nosedive. The Oxford Group became *so* unpopular they tried to disassociate themselves *from themselves* in the public eye. In 1938, they renamed themselves Moral Re-Arma-

---

Group's leader, *fifty years later*.

*The Buchmanites claimed complete innocence. After the war, they announced the matter settled with what they said was a copy of a document found by the Allies after the fall of Nazi Germany. *Time* magazine, with all the resources at its disposal, made a search for and, apparently, never could find any such document in the Allied records. Tom Driberg, in his "The Mystery of Moral Re-Armament," quotes a story that *was found* in the Nazi secret police records that an ex-AA member might find amusing. A Swedish woman who had been angrily denouncing the Nazis, after attending an Oxford Group meeting, felt *guilty* and proceeded to "make amends," writing a letter of apology to the Nazi leader.

ment.

While these events had their effects on the development of Alcoholics Anonymous, probably none affected their doctrine so greatly as the continued public drunkenness of the Firestone heir converted to God-control. One of Oxford Group's biggest public relations coups became, if not for Oxford as a whole, certainly a great embarrassment to their contingent of ex-drunks.

To prevent this embarrassing situation from happening again, AA's public relations were built upon the "spiritual principle" of "anonymity." While "God" had told the Oxford Group it was everyone's duty to give public testimony, God seems to have told the early AA's, very pragmatically, that if people were one night swayed by testimony on the radio, and the next heard how the speaker had gotten drunk, it would hurt His program.

The idea of "anonymity at the media level" springs from Wilson's vision of a chain of alcoholics. AA literature tells of how the founder of AA in Boston drank himself to death but during periods on the wagon managed to carry the message to others. As they tell it,

> "Its founder could never get sober himself and he finally died of alcoholism. Paddy was just too sick to make it. Slip followed slip, but he came back each time to carry AA's message, at which he was amazingly successful... Then came the last bender, and that was it."[57]

Evidently, if people don't know that the bearer of yesterday's message is drinking himself to death today, it doesn't matter. The messenger can do God's work, bring others under God-control and "give to others that which has been so freely given." This is what the early AA members where doing with the radio interview cited at the beginning of this chapter. There was no question of honesty. They were doing what God told them to do. And they were afraid not to. If they didn't have faith in (be obedient to) God and work to bring others into the Program, they would be in serious danger of drinking. To avoid that danger, individual Alcoholics Anonymous members, and AA as a whole, have been very obedient ever since.

When the Big Book was published in 1939, AA membership was about 100. As of 1987, AA reports more than 73,000 groups in 114 countries.[58]

Articles in medical, psychological and alcoholism journals frequently describe AA as "undoubtedly the most successful" qualified with "far and away the largest membership."

But the question remains...

Chapter 2

Does it Really *Work?*

"Keep-coming-back-it-really-works!"

– AA chant

Without a doubt, the general consensus in this country is that Alcoholics Anonymous is an effective remedy for alcoholism and is the treatment of choice. Virtually all treatment centers in the United States funnel their clientele into Alcoholics Anonymous or sister groups such as Cocaine Anonymous.

Rarely, if ever, does the mass media carry anything except the highest praise for AA and the treatment facilities. In newspaper articles, television news features and radio interviews, politicians, movie stars, famous athletes and even an ex-first lady carry the message that they had faced alcoholic ruin but "being in recovery"* saved their lives.

The multi-billion dollar treatment industry advertises

---

*Use of the phrase "in recovery" is an excellent indication of Twelve Step membership. Other indications are use of the word "sober" to mean abstinent and references to amount of time "sober."

the need for "treatment," costs of which can run into the tens of thousands of dollars for a standard 28-day stay.

Each business sells its own treatment as the best for those suffering from what they claim is an incurable, progressive disease. Success rates of as high as 90 percent are reported.

While not all advertisements explicitly state "medical treatment," it is usually implied. While often set in hospitals, rarely is much about the treatment "medical." A small number of alcoholics, perhaps ten or fifteen percent, do need medical assistance for a few days of detoxification. However, any medical attention generally stops there. The stress is on AA indoctrination.

AA members in the early 1940s, according to Jack Alexander in *Life* magazine, claimed 100 percent success with "non-psychotic drinkers who sincerely want to quit."[59]

While the 100 percent claim was questioned, a 75 percent claim was accepted without question and often repeated in the scientific literature and praised as a "remarkable" rate of recovery. The Big Book claims 50 percent at once, 25 percent after some relapses and improvement in the others. They do, however, have a qualifier. These are the rates for those who "really tried."

It seems almost no one subjected these numbers to rigorous examination. The first report of anyone actually doing so apparently appeared on the other side of the world in an Australian medical journal in 1948.

The author, while extolling the virtues of AA, reported that, from his observation, "Only about 10 percent of patients give up drinking at once. The majority of the others may remain sober for weeks or months and then relapse."[60]

Many people have such faith they see no need to actually keep count and perhaps even see the idea of tracking results, of questioning the effectiveness of their "spiritual principles," as offensive. It would be putting science over personal experience (the Fifth Gospel from the Oxford Group).

In medicine, however, the normal course for determining the effectiveness of a treatment is to compare it against other treatment and/or no treatment at all.

There have been two controlled studies of the effectiveness of Alcoholics Anonymous independent of any other type of treatment. Since they deal with persons required by the court to attend AA, they demonstrate the relative effectiveness of AA in a coercive context. Since a significant number of AAs are first indoctrinated in this way, both studies are relevant.

The first was an experiment done in San Diego, California. Chronic offenders, averaging twelve prior drunk arrests each, were given a thirty-day suspended sentence and a one-year probation. A requirement of probation was that they remain abstinent for one year.

A court judge randomly assigned 301 people to one of three categories: no treatment, a psychiatrically oriented community alcoholism clinic and Alcoholics Anonymous. Complete data for a minimum of one year was available on 241 cases. In the no-treatment group, 56 percent were rearrested. The AA group fared the worst. In what was almost a tie with the clinic group, 69 percent of the group sent to AA was rearrested. An interesting question, one that was not answered in the research paper, is whether the clinic, as is customary, also sent their clients to AA.

In the first month, all groups did equally as well (or poorly, depending on how one chooses to look at it). After the first month, presumably when AA or clinic attendance should begin showing its effect, is precisely when both groups lost ground against no treatment. Also, while only eleven of the 241 persons credited AA with their longest period of abstinence, nine of these eleven, or a full 80 percent, were rearrested. *Those who credited AA the most were rearrested the most.* The authors of the report stated,

> "Some of the present writers [3 of 5] were quite optimistic about the possibilities of enforced referral to treatment, but the early encouraging anecdotal reports are not borne out by present data."[61]

In another study of court referral for treatment done in Lexington, Kentucky, 197 alcoholic patients began treatment.[62] They were randomly divided into five groups; professional "insight" therapy, professional behavior therapy, lay-led behavior therapy, AA, and a no-treatment control group. Of the 197 patients who began therapy, 104 were still available for the one-year final outcome study.

Of the subjective measures, perhaps the most telling is the number of respondents who reported improvement for the last three months. AA tied with the no-treatment control group for the smallest percentage of those who could report improvement. One of the professional groups and the lay group fared remarkably better. All groups had some members who attended AA but the lay-led group, which reported the best results on this measure, had the *least* intense AA involvement.

Compounding this pathetic outcome for AA is that the twelve who stuck with AA for the year scored progressively worse on two important MMPI* scales. One of these, the Finney Addiction Scale, is used to identify people who have trouble with narcotics by measuring the qualities such people tend to have. The AA members became more like the kind of people who have narcotics problems.

The other measure, called the Hysteria Scale, is related to people who have somatic complaints and to the denial of difficulties. The AA group, *the group that reported the least success, was also the one most inclined to hide its difficulties.*

The main criticism of these two studies is that they deal only or predominately with people coerced into treatment by the legal system. This, of course, is true. It is also true, however, that they make an excellent case against court-mandated AA attendance.

There apparently have been no controlled studies done of AA against other treatment in a non-coercive environment. So unquestioned has been the effectiveness of AA that most studies comparing treatments compare different versions of AA-based treatment. "Successful outcomes" are often defined, not in moderation or abstinence, but *in rates of AA attendance.* However, some revealing studies have been done.

A most revealing study of the over-all success of AA

---

*Minnesota Multiphasic Personality Inventory

was done by Harvard psychiatrist and prominent authority on the disease of alcoholism, George Vaillant. In one of the longest studies of its size and type, Vaillant followed 100 men for eight years. The men selected were the first 100 consecutive admissions for detoxification at an alcoholism clinic. They were followed up annually. Praised for his candidness, Vaillant wrote of his project in his book, "The Natural History of Alcoholism,"

> "It seemed perfectly clear...by turning to recovering alcoholics [AA members] rather than to Ph. D.'s for lessons in breaking self-detrimental and more or less involuntary habits, and by inexorably moving patients...into the treatment system of AA, I was working for the most exciting alcohol program in the world.
>
> But then came the rub. [We] tried to prove our efficacy. ...
>
> After initial discharge, only 5 patients in the Clinic sample *never* relapsed to alcoholic drinking, and there is compelling evidence that the results of our treatment were no better than the natural history of the disease. ...Not only had we failed to alter the natural history of alcoholism, but our death rate of three percent a year was appalling."[63]

Stanton Peele, an investigator independent of Vaillant's study, after examining some of Vaillant's unpublished data found,

> "Of those who quit drinking on their own, none of the twenty-one men followed up since the end of the study were abusing alcohol. ...*Relapse was more common for the AA group*: 81 percent of those who quit on their own either had

abstained for ten or more years or drank infrequently, compared with the 32 percent of those who relied on AA who fall in these categories."[64]

Despite the fact his own data shows people do worse with AA than without it, in the same book where he presents the failure of "inexorably moving patients...into the treatment system of AA," Vaillant goes into detail telling *how* AA works. Perhaps even odder, he stated,

"...if we have not cured all the alcoholics who were first detoxified over 8 years ago, the likelihood of members of the Clinic sample attending AA has been significantly increased."[65]

Odd indeed, for a doctor to discount not having cured or ameliorated the symptoms of an illness, but to instead boast of getting the patients to join AA. How can this be?

One possibility is that George Vaillant is "God-controlled." He gives indications that this may be so. In attempting to explain the division between those (like himself) who believe that AA works and those who don't, he offers, "[F]or AA to work, one must be a believer."[66]

Perhaps the problem with his alcoholic patients dying at an "appalling" rate wasn't because of a failure of AA but because of a failure on the part of his patients to believe in AA. This is in spite of the fact that those who didn't believe, and wouldn't go, did better.

Also indicative of his being a present-day grouper is that he advises,

"Clinicians and relatives alike need to take the first 'step' of Al-Anon seriously: they must admit their own 'powerlessness over alcohol.""*67

It seems he himself takes the first step seriously and has admitted his powerlessness. Did he take the second? The third? Whether he did or not, he certainly seems to be "working the twelfth." The Twelfth Step is "to carry the message," meaning to work to bring new people into "the program." To this end, George Vaillant, as a *medical* expert on alcoholism, advised in the prestigious Harvard Medical School Health Letter,

"Sooner or later, and preferably sooner, the alcoholic should be induced to attend meetings of Alcoholics Anonymous."[68]

One study of many which indicate *how* AA works in hospitalized patients brings to mind "Oxfordizing" and the five C's. In a Texas hospital[69] 35 men of various lengths of hospitalization in an AA-based program underwent psychological testing. It was found that the longer a patient was in the program the higher he scored on responses indicating defeat, guilt and fear. Perhaps most important, as the patients became more indoctrinated in AA, their self-concept became progressively more negative than when they first sought help for their drinking problems. As the Oxford Group before them, Alcoholics Anonymous uses guilt to bring about conversion to membership. Alcoholics Anonymous has the added benefit of manipulation through fear. With these

---

*This is the same as AA's first step. Al-Anon was originally formed to give the wives of the early AA's an opportunity to "work a spiritual program." It is now available to those who work with, and friends of, alcoholics.

tools at its disposal, indoctrination proceeds. This is all to get a person with a drinking problem to join what has been called, and AA's own statistics[70] back up, "a society of slippers."

The "medical" justification for AA indoctrination used by treatment enterprises and AA itself is the disease theory. Careful examination of disease theory, which many of us have accepted for humanitarian reasons, will show its effects have been far from humanitarian.

Chapter 3

Disease Theory

The idea that habitually drinking to excess is a disease originated with a Dr. Benjamin Rush in the early 1800s.[71] Rush considered intemperance, as well as lying, murder and political dissent, to all be diseases[72] and being a black person a disease symptom.[73] He believed that in habitual drunkards "desire overpowered the will" meaning, in twentieth century terms, that they "lost control." His cure was abstinence.

Rush's ideas were picked up by the growing Temperance Movement. By the 1840s, hundreds of thousands of members of the Washingtonians, a society of reformed drunkards pledged to abstinence, were preaching about their personal experience of loss of control and religious cure.

Of great significance is that, apparently, through the centuries of colonial America, no one ever reported loss of control until one person did so in 1795. Prior to that date, when people drank too much, it was *because they wanted to.*

The Washingtonians soon disappeared but Rush's ideas, enmeshed in strong currents of Protestant Revivalism, were carried through the late 1800s and into the early part of this century. With the collapse of the

Washingtonians, secret societies of abstainers were formed such as the "Most Worthy Scribe of the Sons of Temperance" and the "Independent Order of Good Templars." The Good Templars alone claimed 300,000 members. These groups virtually disappeared in the early 1900s with the development of the movement toward Prohibition. However, the idea that alcoholism is a disease didn't.

Central to today's Alcoholism Movement is Alcoholics Anonymous and the disease theory of alcoholism. Modern disease theory is based on the results of one 1945 survey.[74] The survey consisted of 36 questions thought important by AA members. It was distributed to AA members through an AA magazine, *The Grapevine*. The AA editors of the AA magazine then chose E.M. Jellinek to compile the results. Although Jellinek had some misgivings due to the obvious methodological deficiencies, he felt there was also a great advantage,

> "[A]ll subjects were members of Alcoholics Anonymous. ... [I]t is difficult to get truthful data on inebriate habits, but there need be no doubt as to the truthfulness of the replies given by an A.A. ..."[75]

It seems that the AA members made an excellent choice in the person to compile their data. Jellinek already held their positions as "truthful" and their members as the only creditable source of information about alcoholics.

Out of the 158 questionnaires received, 60 were thrown out either for being incomplete, from women or for having multiple responses on one questionnaire. Without ever investigating non-AA members and without ever checking the results experimentally, the 98 responses from AA members to an AA survey, compiled by an admirer of AA, were used as the factual basis for a disease of alcoholism. This is the present day "science" of alcoholism which supports the disease of alcoholism as espoused by the alcoholism treatment industry and Alcoholics Anonymous.*

The seven major elements of AA's "disease of alcoholism" and their Big Book origins are:

1) **An intense physically based craving is responsible for an alcoholic's "loss of control" of drinking behavior.** From the Big Book comes the cliché, "One drink, one drunk." Dr. Silkworth's ideas on alcoholism are covered in the Big Book. Also in the Big Book are dozens of personal stories that stress the loss of control suffered by alcoholics.

2) **An alcoholic can not be responsible for his behavior when either drinking or in pursuit of alcohol.** The craving takes over normal mental

---

*Some AA members have stated that the concept of disease was foreign to early AA, since it was a spiritual, not medical, program. However, much reference is made to alcoholism being a disease by the earliest members of AA in the Big Book. In telling of her own conversion process one of the "pioneers of AA" says, "I was suffering from an actual disease that had a name and symptoms like diabetes or cancer..." (p. 227) Other early Big Book references by the earliest members to alcoholism as a disease can be found on pages 187, 191, 307 and 308.

function. The Big Book refers to "the subtle insanity which precedes the first drink"[76] and "we were alcoholic and could not manage our own lives."[77] Frequent mention is made of Dr. Jekyll/Mr. Hyde transformations when seized by the obsession to drink or when under the influence.

3) **The disease is progressive and incurable**, with "jails, institutions, and death," the only possible fate unless **lifetime abstinence** is observed. Also from the Big Book, "Over any considerable period we get worse, never better."[78]

4) **Abstinence is unlikely to be maintained without special assistance**. From the Big Book,

> "...make clear three pertinent ideas:
> (a) That we were alcoholic and could not manage our own lives.
> (b) That probably no human power could have relieved our alcoholism.
> (c) That God could and would if He were sought."[79]

In personal story after personal story in the Big Book, AA members say, no matter how hard they tried, until they "surrendered" they couldn't maintain abstinence. Also heavily stressed is, "Alcoholics rarely recover on their own."

5) **The underlying disease gets worse even during periods of abstinence**, meaning that even if one is abstinent, a return to drinking will be to progressively worse drinking, as if one had been

drinking all along. The Big Book tells of the case of a 30-year-old man who was drinking to excess. It was affecting his business so he stopped. Twenty five years later he retired, began drinking again and died within four years.[80] The phrases "Once an alcoholic, always an alcoholic"[81] and "no real alcoholic *ever* recovers control"[82] are among Big Book references to this.

6) **The disease is independent of everything else in a person's life** and has a life of its own. This means people don't abuse themselves with alcohol because of problems in their lives; they have problems in their lives because alcoholism or alcohol has taken control of them. AA's first step, "We admitted we were powerless over alcohol— that our lives had become unmanageable" shows the assumed relationship. Because of this force more powerful than themselves, alcoholics' lives are disordered. Fixing the alcohol problem is assumed to be a prerequisite to fixing any other area of a person's life.

7) **A major symptom of alcoholism and impediment to successful recovery is denial.** Persons afflicted with alcoholism, as a result of "disease processes," deny their problems. Intervention by others, especially those "in recovery," is often necessary for the alcoholic to understand his situation. This element of the disease of alcoholism is not mentioned in the Big Book, at least not directly. Some present-day writers have suggested that early AA didn't consider denial an element of alcoholism.

Certainly the word as used today wasn't in the Big Book. It is, however, implied in the first step. The conversion techniques have always called for confession. Without *denial* of sin, admission (confession) would be unnecessary.

The most important "medical" reason for considering alcoholism a disease is that people do sicken and die from habitual over-consumption of alcohol. When it is pointed out to believers in "the disease" that patterns of alcoholism much more closely resemble habits and compulsions such as nail biting and compulsive gambling, the invariable response is that it is a disease because it is fatal. Of course, car accidents, war and the failure of parachutes to open during free-fall are all fatal too. Are they diseases because they are fatal? Calling something a disease implies a medical remedy. Of course, medicine does have a proper role in all these things. After a car accident, during a war and, in rare instances, after hitting the ground, medical experts are the ones to call upon to take x-rays, give transfusions, set broken bones and carry out other tasks for which they have special training. The same applies to people who have poisoned themselves with alcohol. *The results of their behavior* may well call for medical assistance. But there is no more medical treatment for *the behavior* of excessive drinking than there is medical treatment for careless driving, overambitious world leaders or improperly folded parachutes.

The general public accepted the disease theory more out of compassion rather than a concern for the semantic argument of what is a disease and what isn't. Proponents of the treatment of alcoholism as a disease argued that people with drinking problems should be helped, not jailed. It made sense and still does. The problem and failure has been the nature of the "help."

medicine's answer to the disease

Once alcoholism was defined as a disease, the problem was laid on the doorstep of medicine. AA has been shown to be ineffective but can medicine help?

Many studies have tested this. One particularly simple study done in London[83] had married male alcoholics assigned to one of two groups. One group received the full gamut of medical treatment; psychiatric care, doctors, hospitalization, whatever seemed appropriate during the one year course of the study. The medical services offered were comparable to those available in America. The other group received one hour of common sense advice on how to deal with everyday problems. They were told they were alcoholic, needed to quit drinking and that it was up to them to do so. Both groups had equal AA involvement.* At the end of the year, there was no significant difference between the two groups.

Closer to home, the disease theory has been a tremendous boon to the American treatment industry. Millions of potential clients now have insurance to cover medical treatment. With billions of dollars available, the industry works to convince potential clients of the need for treatment. To capture and maintain market share, individual

---

*The presence of AA in treatment is not so widespread or intense in England as it is here.

corporations work to convince their potential clientele of the wisdom of choosing their particular brand of treatment.

Since ads rarely or never mention AA, it is likely that those in charge of marketing know that if the nature of their "therapy" and "aftercare" was known, it would cost market share. Instead, each business concentrates on the need for treatment and boasts of special expertise, an exceptionally understanding, caring environment and, most of all, exceptional treatment success.

The boasted efficiency of for-profit treatment centers is, at best, misleading media hype. When the data these claims are based on is examined, it becomes clear that the question "Who is in treatment?" is more important than "What is the treatment?" These "scientifically proven" treatment programs are "proven" using biased samples. When the demographics of the test subjects are examined it is found that:

1) they are married
2) they are employed
3) they have higher social and economic status
4) they are younger

All of these factors are indicative of a successful outcome without treatment or in any other treatment.

Also misleading is that those who drop out are not included and a short-term follow-up is used. A three-, six- or twelve-month follow-up may *look* remarkable but, when all factors are accounted for, the amazing 80 or 90 percent becomes equal to every other commonly used treatment and no treatment at all.

Never have the commonly used treatment methods for alcoholism been proven effective. The only evidence for success are the pronouncements of those who have been given the "Keys to the Kingdom"[*] and the promotional sales work of the multi-billion dollar treatment industry.

There is little support for the disease theory among alcoholism researchers. Even people like George Vaillant have major disagreements with many of the elements. It seems that even AA supporters are much less concerned with defending untenable positions than defending the funneling of patients into AA-based treatment programs and on to AA. All of the basic assumptions of the disease theory have been proven untrue.

loss of control

One of the most carefully researched elements of the disease theory is the concept of loss of control. While it may be a common *subjective* experience, it is not physically based, as a wealth of research has shown.

The test most often cited due to its methodological soundness, was reported in 1973.[84] The experiment involved 32 alcoholics and 32 social drinkers as controls. Both groups were treated identically. The 32 alcoholics were divided into two groups. Under the guise of a taste

---

[*]Of course, this language would never be used in public or with new prospects for membership. As the Big Book advises on page 93, "...you had better use everyday language to describe spiritual principles. There is no use arousing any prejudice he may have against certain theological terms and conceptions about which he may already be confused. Don't raise such issues..."

test, both groups were told they would be rating a new product that had not yet reached the market. One group was told they were taste-testing Brand X vodka; the other, Brand X tonic water. In the group told they were taste-testing alcohol, the drinks were mixed in front of them. The catch, however, was that only half actually received alcohol. The other half were poured drinks from vodka bottles which had been filled with decarbonated tonic water. Half of the group that thought they were testing plain tonic water was actually given vodka. For those given vodka in both groups, the concentration was one part vodka to five parts water. It was an amount that would evade detection after use of a mouthwash.

All participants were given two ounces of each of the three different brands as an "introductory sample." This was the priming dose that, according to the disease theory, would cause loss of control. Twenty minutes later, the actual "taste testing" began. Each participant was given three twenty-four ounce decanters, each decanter labeled for a different brand. They were told to drink as much as they needed to in order to rate it.

No one lost control. No one drank all the liquid. The most important result of the experiment was that the amount drunk was determined, not by whether there was alcohol in the drink, but whether the subjects thought there was alcohol in the drink. The ones who thought they were drinking plain tonic, whether they were really drinking alcohol or not, drank about ten ounces. Those who thought they were drinking alcohol drank more than twice as much, whether or not they were in fact drinking alcohol. It made no difference whether they were really drinking alcohol or not. *What made the difference was*

*what they believed and what they expected based on that
belief.*

The loss of control hypothesis has been tested many
times. In another type of experiment, alcoholics who had
to have suffered the DT's* in order to participate were
allowed to drink all they wanted until a certain cut-off
date.[85] Before the cut-off date, *they tapered off on their
own* in order to avoid severe withdrawal. They gave
them boring and tedious tasks to perform in order to earn
"credits" for drinks. *Even when the subjects were going
through withdrawal from prior earned drinking bouts,
drink credits were saved up for later use.*

Loss of control has never been proven and, time and
again, has been shown to not exist.

AA oriented people like to point out that all experimentation has been done under hospital and laboratory
conditions. It has not been done "in the real world."
Somehow the point is missed. The point, as far as the
loss of control is concerned, is that belief and environmental effects are more important than the chemical
effects of alcohol.

"Bad behavior," like fighting with the wife, missing
work, getting in fights, skipping school and committing
crimes, is considered a symptom of the disease. The
possibility that those who, for whatever reasons, are
inclined to break society's rules would be less likely to
obey rules regarding drinking customs is completely

---

*DT's, or *delirium tremens*, is the most severe symptom of chronic
alcohol poisoning and occurs in only the worst cases of alcohol
overconsumption.

discounted. The use of unacceptable behavior as a diagnostic factor in alcoholism has expanded to such an extreme that self-destructive consumption is no longer necessary for diagnosis. Now, as little as one drink a day, never more, may qualify.

The belief that alcoholism is progressive and incurable also has a firm hold on our consciousness even though it has been successfully challenged time and again. One of the first studies to report a return to social drinking by alcoholics was published in 1961.[87] The researcher used extremely stringent requirements in order to avoid error and criticism. The 93 alcoholics in the study had to meet the World Health Organization's criteria for alcoholism. To qualify as having become a moderate drinker, the subject must have *never* been drunk in the years after hospital release. The shortest time period allowed was seven years. He found that seven of the 93 who qualified as alcoholics had returned to moderate drinking.

The announcement created a storm. Everyone knew that alcoholics couldn't return to social drinking. There was something wrong with his study. Two of the criticisms were particularly amusing in the light of the careful restriction used in the categories. One was that the test subjects were never really alcoholics, *they drank too much*, meaning they drank too much to have ever been alcoholics.[88] The other was that the moderation in drinking didn't count because it was *too moderate*.[89]

Other studies have been done since. The largest was by the prestigious Rand Corporation.[90] In a follow-up of 548 alcoholics at eight different AA-based treatment centers, they found that 18 percent had moderated their drinking and become non-problem drinkers after treatment. Only 7 percent managed to abstain for the four year period. Thóse who had some or complete success remaining abstinent, *as a group*, had twice as many drinking-related problems as those who had moderated their consumption. Overall, they did almost as poorly as those who were still problem drinkers at the four-year point. The Rand Reports also pointed out that those who came to believe the "traditional alcoholism ideology" and had successfully adopted the AA self-image of "alcoholic" were the ones most likely to continue heavy, problematic drinking.

Also in contradiction to the idea of the inevitable progression and incurability of alcoholism are studies of the drinking habits of young people. A twenty-year follow-up of college students found it rare for a student who drank until blackout to be doing so twenty years later.[91] Another study followed high school sophomores for 13 years.[92] The data showed that levels of alcohol consumption in the teen years were only *mildly* predictive of later consumption. Teenage abstinence was also found to be mildly predictive of later heavy drinking. In other words, in this study as in others, *abstinence has been found to "progress" to alcoholism almost as well as being a teenage drunkard.*

The concepts of inevitable progression and incurability have great value, great dollar value to the multi-billion dollar treatment industry and, as Dr. Silkworth taught Bill Wilson, great indoctrination value.

Another characteristic of the disease of alcoholism, one which is increasingly being stressed by the treatment industry in their struggle to fill beds, is the symptom of denial. Obviously, those who engage in self-destructive behavior of any type usually have a strong tendency to discount the damage they inflict upon themselves. Denial as used in the disease of alcoholism, however, has a much broader and sinister meaning.

Refusing to turn oneself over to the treatment authorities is denial. One cannot abstain on one's own, they say, so anyone who believes they can is suffering the symptom of denial. Anyone caught in the webs of the treatment/AA system who believes they can moderate their drinking is guilty of denial. Failure to take the full first step of Alcoholics Anonymous, admitting that one is "powerless" and can't manage one's own life, is denial. Either you begin accepting their doctrine or you are suffering a symptom of alcoholism. Stopping drinking is insufficient. One still must accept having the disease and submit to the treatment authorities.

Prior to alcoholism as defined by AA, the only other "social ill" for which denial was considered a symptom was in the Middle Ages. In the "diagnosis" of witches, a sure sign of a woman being a witch was that she denied it. It was based on common sense. A real witch would deny it.

It must have been as difficult for someone accused of witchcraft to argue their way out of it as someone today who, once accused, can't help but "prove" their alcoholism by denying it.

It is important to point out that AA members really believe that alcoholism is a disease with the specific characteristics mentioned here. Much of the reason for this is entirely semantic.

By defining alcoholism as a disease and attaching each of the elements of the disease theory to that definition, it proves itself. Just like the basic assumptions about witchcraft *proved* to almost everyone's satisfaction the existence of witchcraft in the Middle Ages.[93]

Imagine, for instance, the flu redefined as an always fatal disease. If it isn't fatal, it isn't the flu. Now imagine a doctor with a patient who is running a fever, coughing and headachy. If the patient should die, he can be held up as an example of the inevitable fatality of the flu. But what if the patient lives, as is to be expected? He didn't have the flu. How could he have? The flu, by definition, is always fatal. Using such a definition makes it impossible to prove that the flu isn't always fatal. The presence of the same virus and symptoms in those who live and those who die is irrelevant. If it isn't fatal, it isn't the flu.

The definition of alcoholism as believed by AA members and presented to the public operates in the same way. It doesn't matter how many alcoholics have moderated drinking behavior. Using the disease definition, it can't be proved that alcoholism isn't irreversible and progressive. If it is reversed and doesn't progress, it isn't alcoholism.

AA has a semantic method of dealing with the many people who don't fit their model. They aren't "true alcoholics." Whenever anyone returns to "social drinking," the first response of the groupers is that sooner or later "the disease" will get them. They will either return to AA with proper penitence or they will die. Of course this doesn't always happen. When it does, it proves the nature of the disease and wisdom of AA. When it doesn't, it is obvious they never were "true alcoholics."

As with all of life's problems, people with drinking problems sometimes feel as if their lives are out of control. At vulnerable times, it is always helpful to find support until one's bearings are regained. The support can be from friends, family, one's minister, a psychologist or any of innumerable other sources.

Unfortunately, due to the dominance of the AA-and-treatment-industry-serving disease theory, when someone with drinking problems looks for help, all that is found are expensive treatment centers and AA indoctrination.

The heart of the disease theory is the idea that people are helpless to change themselves; to manage their own lives. It denies, in the face of all available evidence, the God-given human potential for growth and change we are all endowed with. It has never been shown that convincing someone they are incompetent to change an unwanted habit or dependence helps them change it.

However, the AA/disease theory of powerlessness through physical/genetic/allergic susceptibility to alcohol *does serve to create an additional dependency, a dependency on AA and expensive treatment centers.* One walks in with what is usually a transitory problem and, if treatment is "successful," the rest of one's life is spent with the belief that, as a defective person, one must faithfully follow most of the Oxford Group precepts or die.*

Much has been said in this chapter about what

---

*This may seem like a strong statement. The particular threats of death implicit and explicit in AA doctrine will be dealt with later.

alcoholism isn't. If it isn't a disease...

Chapter 4

What is Addiction?

The Merriam-Webster dictionary defines alcoholism as "continued excessive and usually uncontrollable use of alcoholic drinks." The definition is quite valid if uncontrollable refers to uncontrollable by others. The record is clear, however, that alcoholics can and do control their drinking when they want to.

Even AA-based treatment centers usually expect alcoholics and addicts to voluntarily stop drinking and using. Publicly funded treatment centers often demand that an alcoholic or addict *stop using before being allowed to enter treatment*. The discrepancy between how alcoholism has been defined and the real-life patterns of alcohol abuse has led one leading alcoholism researcher to say that alcoholism exists "in our language and in our minds, but not in the objective world around us."[94]

Of course, the phenomenon of long-term drinking of alcohol to excess does indeed exist. The problem with the dictionary definition and others is that they are loaded with implied or explicit reasons for, or characteristics of, the behavior.

To keep things in the broadest of perspectives, addiction will be defined here as *the continual repetition of a normally non-problematic behavior to self-destructive excess.* This definition leaves room for a broad range of behaviors including but not limited to: alcohol and drug addictions, "love" addiction, sex addiction, religious addiction, work addiction, compulsive exercise, television addiction, overeating, bulimia and compulsive gambling. This definition also assumes no origin, lifetime course, or resolution for these behaviors. Although no physical cause is implied, there is room for one or, for that matter, any other presumed cause. It is also free of the circular trap inherent in definitions such as "the flu is an always fatal disease." This definition is an empty frame on which to build.

The listed addictions seem so varied.* At first glance, they seem to have little in common except that it defies logic that some people would engage in them to such excess as to cause themselves, and possibly those about them, great harm. With some addictions, the use of a chemical is at the center of the behavior. An inordinate amount of pleasure due to alcohol or a drug seems to be the *cause* of these addictions.

It is often assumed that people derive euphoria, or an inordinate amount of pleasure, from their addictions. In fact, all activities to which people become addicted are rewarding to almost everyone at one time or another.

---

*Ironically, the strongest support for describing such a broad range of behaviors as addictions is likely to come from present-day groupers. Not only do they consider most of the listed behaviors addictions, they also consider most of them diseases.

Many people enjoy the euphoria attached to a drink or two. People enjoy sex. People are thankful for the pain-killing associated with being "high" on narcotics in surgical wards. People find great rewards in prayer or reading religious literature. Many people enjoy exercise, a brisk walk, jogging or working out. A lot of people enjoy occasionally playing cards or slot machines. All of these behaviors are engaged in to some degree by almost everyone. Most of them are considered good for people. This is one strange twist in addiction. Behavior, which in and of itself is harmless, and perhaps even essential to life, is carried to excessive proportions.

Another strange twist is that people in the throes of their addictions are not happy people. They do not enjoy their addictions. We are all familiar with the images of the woman turned prostitute to support her heroin habit, the alcoholic who loses his job and family, the gambler losing his paycheck, and love addict who could be happy if only...

It has been a mystery why people are so compelled. For centuries, labeling these people immoral or weak was thought to explain it. Today, with impetus from the groupers, many people have come to see these behaviors as diseases, but this explanation requires "faith," since every bit of independent evidence contradicts it.

Many modern-day beliefs about addictions are derived from beliefs about the opiates like heroin and morphine. It has been inferred from laboratory studies with animals and the behavior of many addicts that these drugs cause certain bodily changes. It was thought that those changes set up a particular reaction. If a user were to stop, he would soon be in a temporary, but excruciatingly horrible, physical and emotional state. This state, thought to be entirely derived from the chemical, is called withdrawal. Under the duress, or fear, of withdrawal, addicts were thought to be driven to seek out more of the drug. We have held this view for decades.

Without doubt, some people go through severe withdrawal. Some people will do anything for a "fix." Research results, while not contradicting the details, paint quite a different overall picture. One study which contradicts the inevitable addictive power of morphine was done in 1982.[95] Fifty patients who had just completed surgery were allowed to self-administer morphine for their pain around the clock. Even though they used higher doses than street addicts use, some for as long as six days, they didn't become addicted. They didn't suffer withdrawal. *In every case they decreased use of the morphine as their pain from surgery decreased.*

During the Vietnam War, many U.S. soldiers became addicted to heroin. The problem was so widespread many government officials feared what would happen when the troops returned home. There were visions of drug addicts running wild in the streets committing crimes to feed their habits. That didn't happen. After returning home, only about 10 percent had further experience with opiates. Less than 1 percent showed signs of being dependent.[96] It was also found that, of those who didn't quit upon return, 63 percent had already been using narcotics before going to Vietnam.

Rather than looking at heroin addiction as merely a pharmacological effect of using heroin, it is more productive to look at the many other factors that come into play. For instance, what is the effect of the environment?

By comparing the Vietnam Vets with troops stationed in other areas, it becomes clear that being in the war zone, and presumably the associated stress, had a lot to do with whether or not a soldier would become addicted. Soldiers stationed in other areas, like Thailand and Korea, where heroin was available but away from the war zone, had a much lower rate of addiction. It is also noteworthy that even *after* addiction, a change of environment, specifically going home, usually "cured" the soldiers stationed in Vietnam.

Another interesting fact about heroin addiction is that an injection of saline solution will stop the withdrawal.[97] This, of course, only works if the addict receiving the injection doesn't know it is just saline. Also, the severity of withdrawal symptoms depends on the environment. Someone who withdraws in jail may have dramatic symptoms similar to those portrayed in television dramas. However, in other situations, such as certain treatment communities for heroin addicts or in hospital surgical wards, withdrawal is either mild or doesn't exist at all.[98]

Even in non-chemical addictions, like gambling, withdrawal symptoms often appear.[99] Gambling behavior spans a range of intensity from the tourists who lose a few nickels in a slot machine to the most compulsive gamblers who lose their homes, families and even their lives rather than *not* gamble. Of course, with non-chemical addictions, it is difficult to attribute the extremes in behavior to a physical cause such as chemical action or bad genes.

The supposed physical nature of alcohol and drug addiction is belied by the techniques used to determine its existence. There is no test for it. No one can test a blood sample and tell whether a person has a physiological characteristic that defines him or her as addicted. There is no genetic test, or even proven cause and effect connection between any addiction and a physiological difference in anyone. The way addiction is determined is by *asking about* behavior and *asking about* the results of that behavior.

An almost endless series of animal experiments was thought to have proven addiction was caused solely by the consumption of alcohol or drugs. Typically in animal research, great effort is needed to get animals to consume drugs or alcohol. One way this is done is to add alcohol or another drug to the available water. The animals must drink the laced water or die of thirst. Once they become habituated, they continue to drink the laced water even when plain water is added to the cage. This was thought to prove the addictive properties of the drug itself. However, not all the variables were considered.

The severe deprivation needed to induce addiction, and the unnatural conditions needed to maintain it, are not taken into account. For example, for addicted rats housed in groups, which is natural for rats, the consumption of drugs decreased when they had a choice. Those alone in a cage, in solitary confinement, continued to increase their intake even if they had a choice to cut down.[100] Rather than the rats being "slaves to" the chemical, *their chemical consumption was directly related to their environment.*

In one of the cruelest experiments, a monkey is "wired up" so that it can press a lever and inject itself with a drug. The monkey, isolated from others of its kind and restricted from normal monkey behavior, sometimes even strapped to the wall of a cage, will inject itself until death. These studies have been used to demonstrate the addictive nature of *the drug itself.*

A more sophisticated method of getting animals to drink or drug themselves heavily is called intermittent reinforcement.[101] In this method, a rat is fed just enough to keep it always hungry. The hungry rat is placed in a cage where it can get only a tiny pellet of food about every minute. Under these conditions, if alcohol is available, the rat will quickly begin to "drink alcoholicly." If an opiate solution should be available instead, it will become a "drug addict." In either case the rat is subject to be aggressive and to behave bizarrely in other ways, such as eating its litter.*

This appears to be an excellent demonstration of the power of the drugs. Any substance considered addictive can be used and the results will be similar. The only weakness in this model of addiction (which is also its strength) is that *the conditions create excessive behavior.* The behavior isn't caused by the particular chemical available.

Water can be substituted for the alcohol or drug. Rats will consume as much as one-half of their body weight in water in just three hours. They will become aggressive and behave bizarrely. They become just as "addicted to water" as they do to alcohol and opiates. Of course, the roots of the excessive behavior in rats is not in the

---

*The eating of litter referred to here is a condition called "pica." It is not a response to starvation but to stress. The rats were always *hungry*, not starving.

alcohol, the opiate or in the water. It is in the environment and in the rats.

Rats aren't the only animals that respond this way under intermittent reinforcement. Excessive behavior has been brought about in a long list of animals including squirrels, pigeons, monkeys and even humans. Nor is food the only item which can be manipulated to bring on excessive behavior. *Anything needed* by any mammal, including humans, can be used. Water, sex, space or status all can be used to bring about the same effect.

Very little is needed to bring about the excessive behavior characteristic of addiction. All that is needed is for the animal or person to be in a *frustrated state.* Something must be needed which is not available in sufficient quantity but available enough so continued effort will partly fill the need. Giving up must appear to be the worst option. For instance, if rats are given the same amount of food at once instead of a little at a time, they will eat it and give up on finding more. Their behavior doesn't become excessive. It is only in the frustrating gap between enough reward to keep trying and not enough to fill the need that excessive behavior occurs. It can be stated that chronic frustration causes excessive behavior. While over-simplifying things, it can be stated that *chronic frustration causes addiction.*

It might seem difficult to translate laboratory experience into the human experience of addiction outside the laboratory. Humans are different from animals in that, relatively speaking, we live by reason rather than instinct. We learn much faster. Our behavior is much more complex. With our greater abilities, we have an almost unlimited range of possible responses in any given situation. Nor are we so obviously restricted in choice as laboratory subjects. But there are parallels.

For all of our greater skills at reasoning out any situation, we have a matching greater set of needs to fill. A rat may be relatively content with some food, water, companionship from fellow rats and an exercise wheel. People, however, need much more.

Outside of the laboratory, addiction strikes hardest at those who are chronically frustrated in attempts to fill their needs due to an environment which limits choice. Alcoholism, heroin addiction, smoking and overeating are all much more frequent among the poor. The recent crack epidemic is almost entirely an urban poor phenomenon. Poverty is a powerful restricter of choice and a powerful source of chronic frustration. By the same token, the high rate of addiction among U.S. soldiers in Vietnam occurred under an environment of intermittent reinforcement.

The most important thing for any organism is survival. Feeling safe, that survival was not threatened, must have been nearly impossible most of the time in Vietnam. In a war, particularly in a guerrilla war where the whole country is a war zone, there are few, if any, safe choices. The few that were available may have been ruled because they conflicted with loyalty, patriotism or duty. Many troops must have been chronically in a state where no choice was a safe choice but where things weren't so hopelessly threatening as to give up. They were, in terms of producing addiction, much like the rats in an experimenters cage. Instead of food being in short supply, safety was. Like the rats, there was no good choice. The rats had no good choice because there literally wasn't enough food made available and what was available was under intermittent reinforcement conditions. The humans most needed safety. It was at best only sporadically available.

Of course, for the servicemen, safety was just one factor. Physical hardship, being isolated from their loved ones and being at the whim of forces beyond their control all contributed. These factors are breeding grounds for excessive behavior. Once the environment changed, once they were removed from these no-good-choice situations, their addictions faded away.

The hospital patients were in an entirely different situation. They were *removed from* everyday sources of frustration. They were in a temporary situation. Anything of importance *outside* the hospital simply had to wait. Their biggest need was to deal with the post-surgical pain. The solution to the pain problem was self-administered morphine. Although "the drug" is highly addictive, no one became addicted. There were no powerful forces of intermittent reinforcement at work. There was no high level of frustration. Self-administering the drug was an ideal choice for the overriding problem of pain. As the pain diminished the morphine lost its purpose. It might be interesting to speculate what might have happened if the patients had been suffering severe chronic pain. Given a choice, would they have maintained the level of self-administration as needed for the pain? Would they have had a severe reaction to removal of the drug if they had still perceived it as needed? Would they have "craved" it?

Environmental conditions alone fall far short of

explaining addiction in humans. Poor people are more likely to suffer from addictions but not every poor person becomes an addict, alcoholic, smoker or overeater. Only some American soldiers became addicted in Vietnam. Also, sometimes those with the most opportunity and choice, the rich, become addicted.

The environment is important, but the person is more important. Rats in a cage have little or no choice in how to fill their needs. Either the experimenter provides for their needs, ignores them or purposely frustrates them. For human beings even the most deprived environments provide opportunities to fill needs and avoid chronic frustration. Another difference between humans and caged rats is that, except for the people in prison, there are no bars holding anyone in an impoverished environment. A person has no *external* physical restraints preventing him from picking up and moving, getting an education, changing social circles, switching jobs or whatever else may seem desirable.

Human beings, however, often have formidable *internal restraints* which are just as restrictive, if not more so, than prison bars...

Chapter 5

Models

Internal restraints are heavily based in the *perception* of control. An excellent model of the formation and nature of some of these restraints is Seligman's concept of learned helplessness.[102]

learned helplessness

Lessons in which helplessness is learned are among the most damaging for any living creature. An experiment done with dogs demonstrates what happens. Dogs exposed to uncontrollable shock will, after a time, give up trying to get away. They lie helplessly and make no further attempt to escape. Even when placed in a different situation where they could escape, they *don't even try*. What happens with these dogs has been repeated in similar experiments with humans. The response in people is basically the same.

When a human is faced with an *uncontrollable situation*, fear, anxiety or frustration develops depending on the intensity of the unavoidable negative stimuli. As attempts to control the situation fail, the person learns that control is impossible and depression sets in. Punishment will now be taken indefinitely, with no further attempt to escape. Once one learns he is helpless, no further effort will be *wasted* in trying to control the situation. When later confronted with other problems, there is a tendency to generalize the prior lessons of helplessness by giving up more easily. Even if the problem is accidentally solved, a person who has learned he is helpless is unlikely to be able to make the cause and effect connection. His ability to learn has been diminished.

One particularly relevant experiment was done with inner city schoolchildren.[103] The children were chosen because their teachers considered them, due to their consistent failure, incapable of learning to read English. However, in just a few hours, the experimenters taught them to read complete paragraphs of Chinese characters. They didn't know they were learning to read. They didn't know it was wasted effort. They thought they were just associating symbols with words. Since they learned so rapidly it is obvious they were intelligent enough. Evidently they had learned they were incompetent, powerless, to learn to read. As long as they didn't know they were doing the impossible, they didn't know the effort was wasted. They could and did learn to read.

Learned helplessness restricts choices. For instance, if a child learns he is incapable of reading, he will give up even trying to read. Because he gives up trying, he will probably never learn to read. Any option in life which requires reading is simply not chosen. It is "known to be" "unobtainable" and wasted effort. He will also feel inadequate around those who can read and may use it as proof of general incompetence.

It must be remembered that *the restriction in choice is not due to any innate incompetence, it is due to learned helplessness.* It is past experience.

The powerful effect of learned helplessness in *everyone* is demonstrated by hypnosis. When a subject is hypnotized, the part of the mind that knows what is possible and what is not is "asleep." In such circumstances, *everyone is capable of doing the impossible.* For instance, childhood memories can be recalled in great detail, people can make their bodies rigid enough to be laid out between two chairs and then support a heavy person sitting on them, they can change their heart rate and skin temperature and they can walk on hot coals without getting burned.

Learned helplessness clearly limits choice and, in limiting choice, sets the stage for chronic frustration.

a model of the human mind

In the simple model presented here, the mind can be thought of as consisting of two parts: the conscious and the subconscious. The subconscious mind can be thought of as a library or data bank containing everything a person has learned and an automatic system for acting on that information. The conscious mind can be thought of as a control center in contact with diverse areas of the subconscious. It is in the conscious mind that analysis is done and decisions are made.

The conscious mind can deal with only a limited amount of information at a time. However, information is continually processed and acted on outside of conscious focus, in the subconscious.

A good example of the relationship and actions of the conscious and subconscious minds is the learning of complex behavior. When learning to type, a person must consciously consider each particular letter to type, its location and perhaps how hard to tap the keys. With learning, however, this process becomes subconscious. A word is seen and "automatically" entered with no conscious attention paid to the location of the keys, the amount of pressure to exert or even the particular letters making up a word. This is normal human learning, *the grouping of skill and detail together as a subconscious response pattern.* This frees the conscious mind of repetitive detail.

Just as in typing, in the normal course of life most of our action is based upon prior learning and we respond with "pre-programmed" precision to external stimuli. We hear a ringing sound and without thought we go to the door or the telephone, making the distinction without conscious comparison or trial and error. It has long since been thought through. It has long since been learned.

The subconscious has limitations. It is not capable of reasoning. It can only recall what has been learned. *It can only repeat decisions already made in the past by the conscious mind.* For example, if an experienced typist comes across a rarely or never-before-typed symbol, the subconscious can't handle it. It "notifies" the conscious mind of the situation. The conscious mind, with its attention now focused on the problem, will use its own particular skills to analyze and solve it. Should the rare symbol appear often, it will be learned, meaning the subconscious will begin dealing with it automatically.

As has been shown, there is communication between

the two parts of the mind. In learning, information and behavior patterns are transmitted from the conscious mind to the subconscious. The subconscious, on its part, notifies the conscious mind when an automatic learned response is unavailable, when a decision must be made.

The subconscious also communicates with the conscious mind by generating emotion.

emotion

Emotion can be considered to serve two purposes. It draws conscious attention to a situation and prepares the body for expected action. For instance, driving a car, a learned behavior, is done almost entirely automatically. When driving a familiar route, such as a daily drive to work, little conscious attention is paid to the actual driving. The subconscious handles most of the details. Little thought is given to adjusting speed, breaking or making turns. Conscious attention is likely to be focused elsewhere, perhaps planning the day or listening to the radio.

Now imagine a driver's response should a car begin swerving in front of him threatening to run him off the road. The response is a rush of adrenaline, an instantaneous increase in heart rate, an increase in blood pressure and the tensing of various muscles. The subconscious has made a judgement of danger and, in a most dramatic way, gotten the attention of the conscious mind. It has also done much more. It has prepared the body to deal with the situation. Whatever the conscious, reasoning mind decides to do, the body is already prepared to respond quickly.

Emotions are not based in the reasoning part of the mind. They do not normally respond to direct conscious control. For instance, in the driving example, the driver uses the subconscious judgement of danger and preparation for action (fear) to focus attention on the problem and respond efficiently, to take evasive action. When the danger is passed, the subconscious returns the body to its normal state. The heart slows, blood pressure lowers and breathing slows down. The conscious mind's job is to analyze and react on the information provided by the subconscious. A direct attempt by the conscious mind to "get rid of" the emotion, in this case fear, would be doing away with a source of information and preparedness. It would be like closing one's eyes. *Emotions are a special form of awareness and preparation based on that awareness.*

As long as there is proper two-way communication between the conscious and subconscious, any emotional state is either "rationally" appropriate or, as new information is processed, becomes so. Take, for example, a person who is intimidated by computers. He may have learned this fear from others who are also intimidated by computers or perhaps from prior experience with a programming class he failed. Imagine he is told by his boss that the office he works in is to be computerized and everyone must learn word processing. As he attends class, something within the range of two extremes is likely to happen. At one extreme, he would meet with great success in learning to use a computer and wonder how he ever got by without one. At the other, he would be confronted with frustrating, embarrassing or humiliating failure. In the first case, as it becomes clear that a computer makes things easier instead of harder, his emotional response to the thought of using a computer approaches gratitude. The fear response dissipates entirely. In the context of *his* experience, his emotional state is entirely "rational." In the second scenario, fear and intimidation increase. *On the basis of his personal experience,* the emotional response is still "rational." Emotional response has nothing to do with cold, impartial logic. There is no "what one should feel." Emotions are subconscious judgments based on *one's own past experience.* They are also the best conclusions one could arrive at *in the context of one's past experience.*

Human adaptability is very much based on proper communication between the conscious and subconscious minds. Proper communication gives flexibility of response and allows the two separate sets of skills and resources in the subconscious and the conscious minds to work together. This allows emotional responses to "automatically" have a high degree of correspondence with the needs of a current situation.

When something prevents information from being passed to the subconscious for storage, or prevents information from being retrieved, we call it a learning disorder. When someone's conscious mind is not aware of emotional states or doesn't provide accurate feedback to the subconscious we may, depending on the severity, label that person mentally ill.

Chapter 6

Early Childhood Lessons

The impact of early childhood lessons can be best understood from a biological framework. Since human beings, relative to the animals, survive by intellect rather than instinct, a human child's primary biological urge is to *learn* how to survive; *to learn to be like his parents.* In this context, the parent is the supreme, unquestionable authority. Winning parental approval is, in the child's mind, equivalent to being worthy of survival (loveable, good). Parental disapproval, likewise, is equivalent to a message that something about the child is, in some way, unfit for survival (unlovable, bad). Through parental expressions of approval and disapproval, the child learns to see the world, and himself, through his parents' eyes. Barring traumatic events, what a child learns by about age six remains as a framework upon which all future learning is based.

This parental authority, based in a *biological* assumption of parental fitness for both parenthood and survival, is the ultimate measuring stick for the child's perception of his own "fitness for survival/goodness/lovability" or "unfitness/badness/unlovability."

In the "ideal" family, parents have excellent self-images, a good sense of their own self-worth and a system of values that serves them well. They effectively pass these on to their children through modeling, mirroring, warm and loving support, encouragement and confidence in the child's growing ability. In the ideal family, the child learns he is loveable by being loved. He learns he is capable of loving by the warm response of his parents to his loving gestures. Being the ultimate authority, the parents showing of interest and concern for the child, treating the child as valuable, *can't be* questioned. All this is learned. All this is the framework on which future lessons are built.

Children are aware of, and extremely sensitive to, the emotional responses of their parents and they internalize these responses. This is an important way parents pass information on to their children. For instance, if a small toddler tries to put a key into an electrical outlet, a parent's emotional response (fear) is internalized in the child. The child learns when to be afraid. This serves the child well, since mother and father won't always be there to protect him. His recollection of his parent's fear, now his fear, will be sufficient to prevent him from trying it again.

The parent's emotional response, or lack of one, is the core of childhood lessons. If a parent would, in a cool, detached way, say "Don't do that," the child's long term, if not also short term, response would be entirely different. *It is the emotional context and emotional charge that give a lesson meaning, staying power and force.*

When looking at a particular childhood situation it is important to recognize that the emotional response of a parent is much more important than, and overrides, what is said. Context is everything. "Isn't that nice," in response to a child's action, in and of itself, has little or no meaning to the child. The important message is carried in the body language, the tone of voice and the look in the parent's eyes. "Isn't that nice," with an angry glance and tense voice, is a far different message from "Isn't that nice," eyes full of warmth and affection, a relaxed smile, soft voice and maybe a warm hug. Children internalize both the statements and the emotional content, but the emotional content is what defines the words and the event as a whole.

Lessons learned build upon previous lessons and set the stage for future lessons. To learn mathematics, for example, children first learn to recognize numbers without which they couldn't learn simple arithmetic. The knowledge of arithmetic is the basis on which algebra and geometry are learned. Any lower-level error left uncorrected will adversely affect, if not leave impossible, the learning of later lessons.

In the same way, the important building blocks on which children build their view of the world and of their place in it are based on the emotional responses of early childhood authority figures, most particularly the parents. In the first six years of life, a child has basically learned "who he is" through the lessons learned at home. Later experience outside the home tends to merely confirm the lessons already learned.

Our more complex responses, such as what kind of work we do, who we fall in love with, how we raise our children, how we feel about members of other races and the opposite sex, our religion, the foods we like to eat, nearly everything about us, is heavily based upon prior learning, little of which is ever, or ever needs to be, re-examined and changed.

In the ideal family, a child reaches adulthood with confidence in his ability, a healthy respect for and awareness of his needs and an awareness of the surrounding opportunities to fill those needs. Should life circumstances change, new lessons will be learned. The "ideal" person from the "ideal" family is "ideally" adaptable.

Of course the ideal family is just that, an ideal. But,

even in the "average" family, there is a great deal of difference in degree, if not so much in substance, from the lessons usually learned in the family of an addicted person.

Although it has been long suspected, only recently has investigation begun on the connection between severe childhood abuse and the development of addictions. In two studies[104], abuse of illegal drugs by a largely criminal group of adolescents was found to be associated with prior physical and sexual abuse. In a third study[105], severe childhood physical, emotional, and/or sexual abuse was found in 90 percent of the addicts and alcoholics who went through a gay treatment center. The scope of these studies is limited. While of themselves inconclusive, this early evidence supports a connection between an abusive childhood environment and severe chemical addiction in adulthood.

There has also been a wealth of indirect evidence that supports a connection between child abuse and the development of addictions. Among this evidence is the fact that alcoholic parents are the most likely to produce alcoholic or drug abusing offspring.[106] Alcoholic fathers (and one could assume also alcoholic mothers) are more likely to physically and sexually abuse, inflict "cerebro-cranial trauma" and create a home life for their sons of "chronic discord."[107]

Certain parental behaviors and attitudes have also been associated with later addictive behaviors in children. Parents of young adult substance abusers have been described by their children as "cold, indifferent, controlling and intrusive."[108] Independent researchers have found fathers of drug addicts to be rejecting and lacking warmth.[109] Others found that drug abusers come from families in which there was "a communication gap and either laissez faire or authoritarian discipline" and also where the "most powerful parent modeled the use of psychological crutches to cope with stress."[110]

Children at high risk of becoming substance abusers (children of alcoholics, the same group that is so frequently physically and sexually abused and have a chaotic home life) have been found to be "less emotionally controlled."[111] In one study teachers described them as "emotionally immature, unable to take frustration in stride, sensitive to criticism, moody and depressed."[112] Preadolescent sons of alcoholics have been described as having characteristics of "Emotional immaturity, low frustration tolerance, and moodiness."[113]

Children who later become alcoholics have been described as having "antisocial tendencies," "a negativistic outlook"[114] and being "marked by social nonconformity and delinquency."[115] They also have been found to be nail biters, shy, suffer nightmares and phobias, throw tantrums, have tics, stutter, suck their thumbs and have eating problems.[116]

While many outside observers, particularly psychiatrists, often see the behavior of "pre-alcoholics" as evidence of a genetic "predisposition to alcoholism" such as "emotionality," it seems ludicrous to assume that any possible genetic personality predisposition *overrides* being physically, sexually or emotionally abused, growing up with cold, indifferent, rejecting parents or growing up with a parent who is more likely to inflict "cerebrocranial trauma" on their child.

Clearly, not all abused children grow up to be addicted so abuse can't be said to be the only factor in producing addiction. Severe abuse is a "good way" certain lessons are "taught."

At the heart of addiction in humans is learning that *essential* parts of the self are "bad/unlovable/unsuitable for survival." Two of the essential parts taught to be bad are the intellect and internal emotional experience. What happens to children, as may have happened to their parents before them, is that they learn to *not experience*, to *not be aware of*, some or all of their emotions.

For instance, if anger should happen to be one of the emotions considered bad, the child, when displaying anger, will be given the message that to be angry is bad. No distinction may be made for the child, or perhaps even seen by the parents, between the internal experience of anger, the proper and appropriate expression of anger and having a temper tantrum. For instance, if a small child becomes angry and throws food, the child won't simply be given the message that it is unacceptable to throw food. He will be given the message, either explicitly or through implication, that *being angry* is bad. This may be reinforced by the parents' own behavior. They may be so good at "controlling" (repressing) their own anger that the only model the child sees is "not angry" and explosions into vindictive, verbally and/or physically abusive rage. In this situation the child only sees, and therefore learns to consider, anger as a destructive force.

The ways parents express disapproval for the child's experience of anger are as varied as the methods a parent has of showing displeasure. They can vary from physical punishment to verbal disapproval to the withdrawal of affection. Perhaps the most insidious, for a small child, is when a particularly insecure and needy parent is *hurt by* a toddler being angry with them. While pre-adolescents and adolescents often respond quite differently, nothing is so frightening or reprehensible to a small child as a parent being in pain. The child comes to see experiencing anger as betraying his parents. However it may be taught, the small child sees himself responsible and learns that to be angry is to be bad. Anger is far from the only emotion likely to be taught to be bad. A child may be taught that sadness, fear, feeling warmth and affection, and even happiness, are bad and must be suppressed and eliminated.

Child abuse often plays a direct role. Imagine an alcoholic father or mother who regularly gets drunk and beats a child. The child's normal, natural, healthy responses would only serve to provoke further punishment. Under such circumstances, a child may learn to not show or even feel anger, fear or sadness. In the child's mind, if the parent is displeased, the child is somehow wrong and it is up to the small child, with a child's limited intellect, to figure out how.* The lesson to the child may be obvious, "I am bad because I am angry," or sad, or afraid. Every effort is made to be good. He would learn not to be, at least in his conscious awareness, angry, afraid or sad.

In learning to suppress emotion, a child learns to suppress his mechanisms for calling conscious attention to a problem, preparing for action on that problem and processing information for future reference. A child learns to sabotage his mechanisms for awareness, response and change.

A tragic example of learned self-sabotage shows that it is what is learned, not how it is learned, that is important. In this instance the lesson clearly was not a

---

*There are limits to this. It has been reported that if a parent tries to kill or dismember its child, the child will redefine the parent as "bad." However, this evidently must be more than "moderate dismemberment." I know a man whose mother, in one of her often repeated rages expressed at him, cut his finger off when he was three years old. When questioned about his family background, he can give the details, but it is still, over twenty years later, in a framework of, "Well, if I didn't keep my room so messy..." , "Well, if I had behaved..." and, "Yes, but she joined the church and quit doing it." He has never processed, and perhaps never will, that *he was just a little kid, and no little child deserves to have his finger cut off.* The last time I spoke with him he was struggling to stop snorting and injecting himself with speed, which along with other behaviors, continues to prove to him that he is the one who is *bad.*

result of parental child abuse but of a brutal coincidence. Eric M. is an ex-alcoholic now approaching 40. As an 11-year-old child, he was occasionally permitted to move the family car out of the driveway. One Sunday afternoon, he did so without the proper permission of his father who became angry and scolded him. Young Eric, feeling he was being treated unjustly, was defiantly angry. The next day he went off to school still simmering about the dispute. When he returned home, his father was dead. He had suffered a heart attack.

In the boy's mind, reeling with grief and guilt, one idea in particular stuck and stuck fast. Never be angry with someone you love; they will go away. It affected his life in two disastrous ways. First, since a major part of grieving is being angry, he carried that grief with him. Second, he *automatically* suppressed his awareness of anger towards others, especially those he loved. In his mid-30s, he was abandoned after a year-long love relationship. He didn't get angry, at least not consciously. His friends and AA sponsor also abandoned him. His AA "friends" because he was depressed; it upset their serenity. His sponsor accused him of being willful and ungrateful. Eric still didn't get angry.

By this time he had lost twenty percent of his body weight, had not been able to sleep more than an hour or two at night for months and thought he was going out of his mind. He wasn't angry. He just wanted to kill someone. Himself. Because he was afraid to be angry, rather than his anger serving useful purposes, such as providing information and preparing him to defend his person, it nearly destroyed him.

Other lessons assault the child's trust of his ability to reason and use his intuition. When parents make statements about their own feelings that are directly contradictory to the child's keen perception of such things, the child becomes confused. One mistake that parents often make, perhaps in trying not to be cold and unloving as their own parents may have been, is to *always* express love towards their children even at times when they don't feel it. The child, being perceptive to the real emotional state, is thrown into confusion.

If the child doesn't question further, he will be trapped into figuring out how he is wrong. Either his perception is wrong or his parent really doesn't love him. If he believes his perception wrong, he comes to distrust his intuition. If the child comes to the conclusion that the parent doesn't love him, the parent being the measure of what is right, he has no choice but to see himself as unlovable. If he questions the parent and gets the message that his *awareness* is displeasing, he may learn to not be aware. He will learn to "automatically not notice." He will make the conscious decision to pretend not to notice and practice it until it becomes subconscious. Later in life, he may well wonder how he could have been so gullible as to fall for a woman who didn't love him or how he could be so wrong in sizing up business partners.

Assaults may be directed against the child's trust in his ability to use his reason, to think. When parents criticize their child's ability to think, the child internalizes his parents statements and their emotional context. They are internalized as the child's own thoughts and feelings toward himself. If criticism is severe enough, the child may learn he is *helpless* to think. He'll learn to "automatically" *not try* to think things through.

In the addictive family system, children often learn other lessons which diminish their capacity to fill their needs later in life. Some of the lessons which cause the most trouble are those directly surrounding basic lovability and fitness for life. When parents are incapable of loving their young child, the child doesn't see it as the parents' problem. He is left to figure out how he is wrong. He can either think, "There is something wrong with me; I am unlovable" or "There is something wrong with me; I shouldn't want to be loved," or both.

In the same way a child learns he is unlovable, he may learn he is incapable of loving. If parents are incapable of being touched by their child's displays of love, again the child is in the position of figuring out how he is wrong. He can either think, "There is something wrong with me; I am incapable of loving right" or "There is something wrong with me; I shouldn't want to love."

Since in early childhood parental love is equivalent to a message of fitness for survival, fitness for life, a child who learns he is unlovable is in for serious problems. Just like the hungry rats in the cage who could never get quite enough food, these children are subject to never in their lives get enough love and approval. They tend to spend the rest of their lives compensating for their "unfitness" or "unlovableness." They've already been taught that their emotions are wrong. As long as they don't allow themselves the awareness of the emotions involved in the lessons of unlovability, the lessons can't be relearned correctly. Since the lessons are kept buried away, they can't be challenged. What the adult normally does is everything possible to prove his fitness in his parents' eyes. He can be not angry, not sad, not afraid or not aware.

The lessons which interfere with later love and intimacy vary tremendously. If parents ignore their children, the children build their world view on the belief that they should be ignored, that they are not worthy of attention. In adulthood, they may be confused by others showing them attention. The *subconscious judgement* may be made; "Something is wrong with them. They think I'm worthy of attention," or, "What am I doing wrong that I'm drawing attention." A parent may ridicule a child for any demonstration of a desire for, or expression of, affection. In such cases, as an adult, he may ridicule those who try to show him love and affection.

Parents who are unable to express love and affection may substitute other things for love. For example, instead of expressing love for their child by hugging, caressing, and other warm and affectionate interaction, they may, out of a sincere attempt to love their children, buy them things instead. A child who grows up under such circumstances may, as an adult, "do everything for" someone they care about and wonder why they don't get anything in return. Of course, "everything" doesn't include giving genuine warmth and affection and the "love object" is not chosen with a consideration to his or her ability to give and appreciate warmth and affection but for the willingness to accept material goods.

One important area to cover before moving on to adulthood is the role of God in the addictive family system. Parents, as the ultimate authority, define God for their children. The child's view of God is in large part an image of the values of the parents. In the "ideal" family, God plays a central role in the child's feelings of self-worth and is seen as a loving and kind protector; as an extension of parental love. In the addictive family system, God is often used by the parents to enforce discipline. Veiled and not-so-veiled threats of eternal damnation are made by the parents in order to enforce rules which can be enforced in no other way.

In families where essential parts of the natural internal experience of thought and emotion are taught to be evil, God's role may be cast as the "thought and emotion police." For example, if a child is suspected of having thoughts unacceptable to the parents, the child may be told it is displeasing to God and that the child must not think them if he wants to go to heaven. Of course the child knows the alternative to heaven is hell. In the family in which children are taught the parental belief that anger, in and of itself, is bad, religion will be selectively used to enforce the family rule. For instance, if such a family happens to be Christian, the children will never be told about Christ's anger when throwing the moneychangers out of the temple.

To the child in such dysfunctional families, God is seen as an agent of the abusive parent and God's love is seen as parental "love." For instance, imagine the effect on a ten-year-old girl who on Saturday night is beaten by her drunken father. Sunday morning she goes to Sunday school class. Imagine the message *she* gets when she hears the teacher read from the Bible, "Honor thy father and thy mother, that all may be well with thee and thou mayest live long on the earth." God, in the child's mind, is on the side of a man who has just beaten her and, if she doesn't honor him, God will kill her. Hardly the message intended.

Children who have learned to disrupt their normal mental functioning may never in their lives be directly critical of their parents' actions in early childhood. They are even less likely to question the lessons learned as a result of those actions. However, they may have such a negative concept of God that, at the first opportunity, and quite understandably, they reject God and religion as terrible oppressors.

.

Chapter 7

The Adult

The adult in the addictive family system tends to have severely limited awareness. In childhood, particularly early childhood, he knowingly struggled to not be angry, sad or afraid. In adulthood, he operates "on automatic." By then, lessons may have been so well learned that, only at times, is there so much as a vague sense of anxiety, or perhaps a sense of emptiness. When "bad" emotions do manage to "leak through," they aren't viewed as important information or preparation. They are more likely to be a source of confusion or fear; they shouldn't be there.

One reason emotional experience continues to be seen as "bad," even after adult reasoning ability has developed, is that, having a history of being suppressed, the emotions are "behind the times." Imagine, for instance, a bright child who has learned he is intellectually incompetent. Any attempt to "be smart" in school brought humiliation from his peers.

Later in life he may feel anxious or fearful when faced with an exam. Even though circumstances are different from those in childhood, the same feelings are subject to surface based on the similarities. He knows his feelings are "wrong" and an "interference." He will make every effort to suppress, ignore and/or discount them. By suppressing his fear and anxiety, by refusing to be aware of a wealth of subconscious information, he never learns to "automatically" discriminate between childhood situations where he was humiliated and similar situations in adult life. The subconscious continues to act on the old lessons. "I am stupid and will be humiliated."

In "normal" functioning, the subconscious would generate fear and make pertinent information on similar past situations available to consciousness. The conscious mind, in response, would focus its attention on the problem. Knowing why the fear was generated, it would be able to reason out the situation. Awarenesses such as "I am well prepared. I will do fine," "These are different people. Even if I do poorly, they won't ridicule me" or "I've shown myself I'm not stupid, but smart by..." The subconscious, having gotten conscious attention, is ready to listen, ready to learn. In this way, perhaps immediately, perhaps over time, the subconscious learns to discriminate between past and current situations.

The "addictive personality" operates in quite a different fashion. The generation of emotion is seen as the problem. The real problem is seldom recognized and even more rarely dealt with. Even worse, when the feared humiliation doesn't happen, it is seen as proof of the "wrongness" of the fear. This assures that continuing action is taken which keeps the functioning and the contents of the subconscious far below potential.

The "addictive personality" bypasses learning, growth and normal human functioning.

Restricting one's ability to feel and deeming one's feelings "inappropriate," severely limits the ability to fill needs or *even be aware of them.* For example, if someone has been punished in childhood for being successful, is warned against the terrible things that will happen if he succeeds or is taught the "futility" of trying to succeed, success may well be avoided in adulthood. Even if attained, the anxiety may be so intense that success is an extremely unpleasant experience. In such circumstances, in order to make the anxiety go away, the success will be thrown away.

In a similar way, if a child learns that to feel good is "bad," the adult will automatically avoid feeling good. While conscious effort may be focused on some goal, the subconscious will, outside of conscious awareness, act on the "old lessons." It will sabotage the conscious efforts to feel good, which it holds as a dangerous condition.

Perhaps the most severe internal restrictions typical of addicted people involve emotional intimacy. People who are taught, and continue to believe, that normal human emotional response is to be suppressed have severe problems with closeness. To the degree that a person is unable to experience and to express anger, sadness, fear, happiness and other feelings, he is unable to be intimate with friends and lovers.

This is at the root of the loneliness often experienced by addicted people. Even if in a room full of people, not being able to communicate with themselves, not being with themselves, they can't communicate, can't be with, others. *No relationship with another human being can be less superficial than the relationship one has with oneself.*

Other important restrictions are those caused by learned helplessness. Just like the perfectly capable child who learns he is incompetent to read, the addicted person may learn that he is incompetent to succeed in important areas of his life and hence give up trying. For instance, he may learn he is incompetent to earn a living, make friends, be attractive to the opposite sex, love somebody, be loved, be a desirable party guest, maintain a marriage, appreciate art or music, get along with the boss or be happy.

Once people learn helplessness, they have difficulty making the associations which prove the belief untrue. For instance, if a boy learns he is too uncoordinated to play football, even if he should become a video game whiz, he will be unlikely to make the connection. If he had begun making the association while learning to play video games, he likely would never have become a skilled player. He would have given up because he believed that to try to excel at something which requires coordination was a wasted effort.

When attempts to fill a need do not fail often enough for helplessness to be learned, but do fall short of filling the need, a chronic state of frustration occurs just like that of the rat in the cage under intermittent reinforcement. Having learned to sabotage normal mental functioning, the person may be unable to recognize, much less fill, his needs. As a matter of fact, he may see avoiding the awareness of certain or all emotional states as a *primary* need. Under these conditions, somewhat less severe than total helplessness (paralyzing depression), excessive behavior will be engaged in.

A generally transitory form of this often occurs with the death of a spouse or divorce. It is not unusual for someone who has suffered such a loss to either experience extended depression, to drink to excess or behave excessively in other ways. Normally, after a period of weeks, months or maybe years, feelings are processed, hope is regained and efforts are made to directly fill the "empty place" in their lives. The difference between someone who drinks to excess due to temporary feelings of hopelessness and frustration and those who drink due to chronic, lifelong feelings of hopelessness and frustration is the difference between transitory alcohol and drug problems and "having the disease of alcoholism."

Psychological tests point out some important characteristics of those with severe chronic drinking and drug problems.

The Minnesota Multiphasic Personality Inventory (MMPI) is one of the most widely used tests for psychological diagnosis. It is made up of 566 true/false questions. It is designed to detect attempts at both "looking good" and outright lying. Various "scales," or subsets of the 566 questions, have been used to distinguish persons with various types of "pathology."

The MacAndrew Alcoholism Scale[117] was designed in the early 1960s to separate alcoholics and drug addicts from psychiatric patients. Due to its high rate of accuracy, it is still in use today. Drug addicts and alcoholics from ages 18 to 70, average age 42, differ significantly in their responses to 49 of the 566 MMPI questions.

They see themselves as "bad." They are more likely to agree with the statement, "I deserve severe punishment for my sins."

Their levels of self-awareness are lower than that of psychiatric patients. It is so low, in fact, that they are either ignorant of, or discount, even physical pain. While they report more coughing and vomiting blood, they also report they feel little or no pain.

In terms of awareness of emotional factors underlying their behavior, they are more likely than psychiatric patients to agree with the statement, "Evil spirits possess me at times."

Probably the clearest examples of diminished awareness in alcoholics is how they see themselves and their parents. One need not look far to find examples where early childhood "self as bad/parent as good" lessons are carried into adulthood with a total blindness to the extremity of the childhood situations. Two of the best examples, due to their celebrity as alcoholics, are Bob Smith and Bill Wilson, the co-founders of Alcoholics Anonymous.

In the first "personal experience" story in the Big Book, Bob Smith describes his parents,

"My father was a professional man of recognized ability and both my father and mother were most active in church affairs. Both father and mother were considerably above the average in intelligence."[118]

In his life story, an A.A. approved book, a quite different, although not necessarily contradictory, picture is painted. Evidently, his mother was a stern religious fanatic who spent her time obsessively with the church and had little time for her only child,

"Mrs. Smith ... was described as a stern, tight-lipped, churchgoing lady who busied herself with the countless social and religious activities of [her church]."[119]

"Mrs. Smith felt that the way to success and salvation lay through strict parental supervision, no-nonsense education, and regular spiritual devotion."[120]

Contrasting with this outwardly pious attitude was a cold, indifferent woman who had little concern, much less love and affection, for her son.

"Grandma Smith [Bob's mother] was a cold woman. ...Once she came to the house, and we were all sick with the flu. Instead of pitching in, she went to bed, too!"[121]

"Young Bob was sent to bed every evening at five o'clock. He went with a quietly obedient air that might have led some parents to suspect the worst. When he thought the coast was clear, Bob got up, dressed, and slipped stealthily downstairs and out the back door to join his friends. He was never caught."[122]

One could deduce from this information that young Bob Smith's sneaking out was an early sign of rebellion and leave it at that as the AA writer cited here apparently did.[123] However, it seems extremely strange that parents would send their child to bed at five in the afternoon. It also seems strange that they would *never* check on him and find him missing. Also rather odd is that they wouldn't notice his suffering lack of sleep if he wasn't expected to spend more than eight hours or so in bed. It seems far more likely that "out of sight, out of mind" was the rule. Of course, a child treated like this thinks he deserves it, that parental treatment is right. In spite of unloving, rejecting parents, Bob Smith describes himself, directly after his description of his parents as intelligent and church-going, like this,

> "Unfortunately for me, I was the only child, which perhaps engendered the selfishness which played such an important part in bringing on my alcoholism."[124]

The other co-founder, Bill Wilson, is reported to have had a close relationship with his father.[125] Bill's father, who had drinking problems, was himself a child of a heavy drinker.[126] His mother was in poor mental health and suffered a series of "nervous breakdowns" and went to a sanitarium at least once.[127] When Bill was six years old, he wrote a letter to his mother who had already been away some months, probably "recuperating." In the letter he indicated how he saw himself, "I want to see you ever so much. I try to be a good boy."[128] Evidently, as is typical of young children, he believed his mother's return, and his being able to re-experience her affection, to be contingent upon his being good enough. Bill remembered himself as being friendless at this time because "his shyness and awkwardness prevented him from developing close friendships..."[129]

Bill eventually got his wish and his mother returned home, at which time she announced that Bill's father had "gone for good." Bill didn't see his father again for nine years. The exact age this occurred is not given in

Wilson's autobiography but was no later than age 10 or 11. Bill later told of hearing that he wouldn't see his father again. "It was an agonizing experience for one who apparently had the emotional sensitivity that I did."[130] He saw his sensitivity as being part of the problem. He could not, and apparently never did, see his sensitivity as being a perfectly natural and normal response to abandonment by the father he loved. He says, "I hid the wound, however, and never talked about it with anybody..."[131] Turning to his mentally disturbed mother was out of the question. She "lacked the warmth and understanding"[132] Bill needed. This may have been putting it mildly because as Bill remembers her at this time, "My mother was a disciplinarian, and I can remember the agony of hostility and fear that I went through when she administered her first good tanning with the back of a hairbrush. Somehow, I never could forget that beating."[133] His mother soon left after recuperating from some unspecified illness. Bill was now abandoned by both parents. He sank into a year-long depression.

Bill stayed with his maternal grandparents. He loved his grandfather, but also recognized that, "they were not overpopular people."[134] At some point Bill began to excel both scholastically and athletically. At 17, he fell in love with the minister's daughter, Bertha. Unfortunately, she died "suddenly and unexpectedly." This great loss precipitated a "tremendous depression" which lasted for three years. His grades suffered and he no longer was an overachiever. As he later told it, "No athletics, no schoolwork done, no attention to anyone. I was utterly, deeply, and compulsively miserable, convinced that my whole life had utterly collapsed."[135]

Bill was never again able to maintain success after this loss. He later told of his thoughts at this time, "I could not be *anybody* at all. I could not win, because the adversary was death."[136] While he certainly had been winning in scholastic and athletic terms, in the more important terms of parental love and romantic love, he had lost big. In the future, whenever he was faced with success, he'd go off on a drunk and ruin it.

One facet of the denial of prior abuse and the viewing of "the self as bad/parent as good" is that, quite often, the substance abuser is openly hostile toward one or both parents. While the very early childhood lessons are the ones most sacrosanct, other factors come into play. One is that maltreatment is more easily recognized in the teen years. Also, older children, having a more developed intellect, are not as locked into the position of seeing themselves as wrong as is the small child. It is the *emotionally unrecognized* abuse that teaches the child that he is "bad" or "defective" that does the most damage.

Another factor is that abused children often become most attached to, and identify with, the most abusive parent. An example of this is a man named Angelo who had begun irregularly attending AA meetings. Angelo, who was around thirty at the time, was extremely skilled at "proper" upper middle class social interaction. He dressed tastefully, was careful to use perfect grammar and pronunciation and never used bad language. For several months he expressed great anger toward his stepmother, whom he characterized in negative terms, but his deportment and language was always "proper." He described his father and his relationship with him in glowing terms. For months Angelo expressed great fondness for his father. I sat over coffee with him one night for three hours. During the entire time, he told me story after story about what a perfect father he had.

Not long afterward, I ran into him again at "after meeting" coffee. His demeanor and behavior had changed radically. No longer was he worried about being "proper." He was boiling over with rage. Face red, eyes blazing with hatred, he spoke in an entirely uncharacteristic fashion, "That fucking bastard. He used to beat me every time he got drunk. I want to kill that fucking bastard." He went into detail about the sometimes bizarre, always cruel, punishment he had suffered at the hands of his father. After a long time of expressing his rage, as he began to calm down, he began reverting to the "old Angelo." He became concerned with his "unsightly display" and said he felt like some sort of horrible monster. Unfortunately he was among a group of AA members who, although a little more "liberal" than most, shared the wisdom that he *was* "half-way" a horrible monster.*

For people with various learned attitudes towards themselves of learned helplessness, distrust of intuition, contempt for their emotions and a general basic distrust of *themselves*, drinking alcohol, as well as other addictive behaviors, can have much to offer...

---

*In AA theology, allowing oneself to experience anger is considered a sin and a leading cause of returning to drinking. Unfortunately, at the time I was an AA member and had nothing to say. It might have been appropriate to ask who the horrible monster was, a parent who beat and tortured his child year in and out, or the beaten and tortured child. As I'm writing I wonder if he ever "made amends" to his father for being angry with him as AA members are expected to do.

Chapter 8

Drinking

In a purely physical sense, alcohol intoxication can be considered to be an across-the-board incapacitation of normal brain function. Depending on the degree of intoxication, people have difficulty speaking clearly, accomplishing tasks like driving and walking, thinking, remembering and committing new experience to memory. The desire for this disruption of normal mental processes is at the heart of both social drinking and alcoholism.

While there are specific pharmacological effects of alcohol that contribute to social and alcoholic drinking, these are of little relative importance except as a general backdrop for *expectancy effects*. This is demonstrated in a rather humorous anthropological study done among the natives of the Truk Islands in Polynesia.[137]

Young males, not knowing one must *drink* alcohol to get drunk, became "intoxicated" by *sniffing an empty bottle*. They "lost control" of their behavior because they knew from seeing drunken outsiders what happened when people got drunk.

Because they were intoxicated, the village elders declined to punish them. Obviously the behavior was attributable to the alcohol, not the young men.

While this may seem extremely far-fetched, there is ample concrete evidence that what is believed about the effects of alcohol, or other drugs, to a very large extent overrides the actual physiological effects of the chemical in terms of behavior and subjective experience.

In a study using hypnosis with heroin addicts, experimenters were able to produce, *by suggestion*, a drug "high" in their subjects complete with physiological changes such as altered pupil size and blood pressure.[138] They also produced the withdrawal state *by suggestion*. The subjects, when actually given drugs and drug-counteracting posthypnotic suggestion, behaved normally. In other words, people can become, for all practical purposes, high on drugs and go through withdrawal from those drugs *without ever taking them*. They can also *behave as though not high* when actually on drugs.

A special method called the *balanced placebo design* has been necessary to determine the effects of alcohol itself as opposed to the effects of believing that alcohol has certain effects. Subjects are divided into two groups. One group is led to *expect* that they are drinking alcohol. The other is led to *expect* that they aren't. Every effort is made to build expectancy, such as mixing the drinks in front of the subjects and demonstrating false "breathalizer" results. Both groups are divided in half again. Half of each group is actually given alcohol and half not. The four groups are:

1) believe alcohol, given alcohol
2) believe alcohol, given no alcohol
3) believe no alcohol, given alcohol
4) believe no alcohol, given no alcohol

Use of this experimental design has disproved many widely-held beliefs thought proven in earlier experimentation. Among these beliefs about alcohol is that alcohol causes sexual arousal.

In a study with the balanced placebo design, male social drinkers were divided into the four groups listed above.[139] The subjects were wired to equipment which measured several factors in sexual arousal including penile tumescence, heart rate and skin temperature. After drinking, the subjects listened to tape recordings of heterosexual intercourse, forcible rape and nonsexual sadistic aggression. The two groups who *believed* they had drunk alcohol were more aroused by the rape and sadism tapes than the other two groups. Belief, not actual alcohol consumption, was the deciding factor.

Another experiment with the balanced placebo design used "dirty pictures" of varying types; some "deviant" and some "normal."[140] The subjects were timed on how long they spent looking at the individual pictures. Those who *believed* they had been drinking alcohol, as a group, looked at the "deviant" pictures longer. In other data gathered from the subjects, it was found that only those who had a high level of sexual guilt were affected by the belief that they were drinking. This indicates that, rather than alcohol "unleashing perverted sexuality," the *belief one has been drinking* counteracts sexual guilt.

The main effect of alcohol on human sexuality is to decrease physiological response. But, *believing one has been drinking* more than counteracts decreased physiological sexual response by "giving permission" or "displacing responsibility" for one's behavior from oneself to the alcohol.

The belief that alcohol causes aggressive behavior is also widely held. In another experiment with a balanced placebo design, experimenters found,

"The only significant determinant of aggression was the expectation factor: Subjects who believed they had consumed alcohol were more aggressive than subjects who believed they had consumed a nonalcoholic beverage, regardless of the actual alcohol content of the drinks administered."[141]

Another study found that those who *believed* alcohol increased aggression were more aggressive when they thought they were drinking. This held true even after taking into consideration how hostile the subjects were to begin with. In other words, no matter how hostile a person may or may not be, if he *believes* drinking will make him more aggressive, he will be more aggressive if he *thinks* he is drinking.

The effect of expectancy on behavior when drinking is profoundly highlighted in different South American Indian tribes. Different tribes have different attitudes and beliefs which govern their drinking behavior. One tribe may use alcohol strictly on religious occasions. In a religious ceremony, the priest may get so drunk he needs help standing up. However, nothing detracts from the completion of his priestly duties. There is neither aggressiveness nor licentiousness. No behavior is *expected* to detract from the spiritual nature of the occasion. None does.

A few miles away, another tribe, with more outside influence, may become rowdy when drinking at a nearby *cantina*. Another nearby tribe may combine the two, behaving piously when drunk at religious ceremonies and losing all restraint on social occasions.

The general attraction of alcohol in our culture is heavily based on its use as a "social lubricant." Alcohol, like Valium, the barbiturates and certain other drugs, is an anti-anxiety agent.[142] It decreases certain types of fear such as fear of failure, punishment and frustration. A drink or two will lessen or remove the little fears which inhibit social interaction. For example, if someone is a little afraid of striking up a conversation with a stranger because they are somewhat worried about rejection or "saying something stupid," alcohol will weaken the fear and allow spontaneous interaction. Alcohol also narrows awareness in general and decreases self-awareness.[143]

For instance, the attention of a partygoer is apt to be narrowly focused on the party. The frustrations of the workday, worries about tomorrow and awareness of the self fade away as attention is narrowed to the competing music, conversation and food. This is the core of the expectations and goals of social drinkers.*

There is no one reason some people see benefit in drinking excessively over other excessive behaviors. In the following paragraphs some of the more common perceived benefits of drinking are presented. *The degree that the benefits of alcohol are only perceived benefits and fail to fill real needs is the degree to which alcohol use is a problem.* For example, the light social drinker seeks only a moderate amount of disinhibition and "euphoria" from alcohol and only on certain occasions. He generally gets exactly what he expects. He is also likely to expect that alcohol will intensify all feelings, pleasant as well as unpleasant.

Heavy drinkers, on the other hand, perceive great benefit in drinking to excess. Unlike social drinkers who tend to expect alcohol to intensify whatever they feel, alcoholics commonly expect to feel better no matter how they feel.[144] Under such expectations, the worse one feels the more *reason* one has to drink. If a heavy drinker is fighting the emergence of unpleasant feelings of enough intensity and persistence, he may drink so much his friends will have to tell him the next day how much fun he had.

Drinking to dull the awareness of undesired feelings does nothing to remove the cause of those feelings. A

---

*This narrowing of awareness is not necessarily a pleasant experience. A social drinker usually drinks in a pleasantly stimulating environment. An alcoholic who is sitting alone in a bar, a situation a social drinker rarely finds himself in, may focus his attention on something sad and "cry in his beer."

woman who drinks to suppress feelings of anger or jealousy over a suspicion her husband is having an affair will never, by drinking, find out if her suspicions are justified and appropriately deal with the situation. Instead, she may keep her suspicions, anger and jealousy in perpetuity. She would have "a need" to drink many times over one situation.

Drinking alcohol can also be a way of temporarily evading *internal* restrictions. People "know" alcohol causes aggressive, hostile behavior. Since "the alcohol causes it," a mild-mannered gentleman who never has an unkind word for anyone can, by getting drunk, give vent to his hostility. Everyone, including himself, "knows" he would never act that way; it was the alcohol. He preserves his self-image. Alcohol serves a "useful" function.

Everyone "knows" that alcohol decreases inhibition and breaks down resistance to sexual advances in women, "Candy is dandy but liquor is quicker." With this knowledge, a prim and proper lady who would never be sexually seduced can be seduced into drinking and, the next morning when she wakes up in a strange bed, can tell herself, "I shouldn't have drunk so much. Look what happened to me." She knows she isn't a "loose woman." It wouldn't have happened if it wasn't for the alcohol.

It must be made clear that because of alcohol's scrambling of normal mental function, it is possible someone will be extremely aggressive or promiscuous due in part to the effects of alcohol — one time. The issue here is not the spurious, one time, "freak" incident but the continual repetition of the same behavior.

The point in these two instances is not that people consciously set out to use alcohol as an excuse but that people who have been taught to deny vast areas of their own existence easily fall into a further trap. They come to *attribute their own power and their own choices to external forces*. For instance, the man who repeatedly gets drunk and beats his wife or the woman who gets drunk and "is taken advantage of" every Saturday night will ruefully blame the alcohol and swear never to drink again. However, no matter how sincere, neither is likely to keep their promise.

They will try to be good in early childhood terms. They will work to keep their mental function disrupted. The angry and abusive man will try not to feel angry, the promiscuous woman will try not to feel lonely. Against the certainty he or she will become angry or lonely, alcohol may seem a "good" solution. Alcohol may come to be "automatically" seen as the solution. The more incapacitated mental function is, the easier it is to be "good." Even if failures occur, like becoming abusive or promiscuous, it can't be helped, "the alcohol was responsible." It is a better choice to risk becoming abusive or promiscuous than facing the certainty that anger or loneliness will reappear and no one but oneself is to blame.

By considering emotions the problem and believing that drowning them is the best possible choice, it is unlikely the proper associations will be made. The hostile man may never know the real causes of his anger or productive ways of expressing it. The promiscuous woman may never recognize her loneliness and find methods of relating to men that are more honest and more consistent with her values.

Repressed anger and intimacy problems often play a role in alcoholic drinking. However, the "misbehavior" is usually much more associated with temporary and increasingly futile attempts to escape from learned internal rules and regulations.

These internal restrictions are ones that other people simply do not have as opposed to "society's rules." For example, if someone has been taught they don't deserve to be happy, they can break the rule and be "happy" by becoming drunk. The anti-anxiety effects of alcohol decrease the fear of punishment and the alcohol can be *blamed*. If someone has learned to stifle their spontaneity, by being drunk, they have *internal* permission to be spontaneous. Again, the alcohol is responsible, not the person.

If someone is taught in childhood that they don't deserve to be happy, but to be punished, he can temporarily evade the injunction by getting uproariously drunk and having a good time, then spend the next day "making things right" by suffering a hangover.

Alcohol has many perceived benefits for heavy drinkers other than permission, or as an excuse, for "misbehavior." People who have been led to believe they are incompetent and fear the possibility of exposure, particularly to themselves, can use alcohol as protection from the feared "truth."[145] For example, someone who fears he is incompetent in the business world may prefer to risk causing failure by drinking too much rather than *face the fear* that he may indeed be incapable. It is a perverse kind of win-win situation. If he fails he can blame the drinking. If he succeeds, he can give himself "extra credit" because it was so much more difficult with the handicap. For the serious self-handicapper, there is almost no limit to the variations of this method which can be used. It can be used at work, at play and in relationships.

Perhaps the biggest motivation for excessive drinking is to cope with "negative" emotional states. Alcoholics and addicts of all types see the internal experience of emotion, as well as other integral parts of the self, as bad. The "solution" is to keep the offending emotions out of awareness.

At times when "bad" emotions are subject to be aroused, alcohol consumption increases. One interesting study investigated "heavy social drinkers"* who were provoked to anger with and without an opportunity to retaliate.[146] The sixty drinkers were intentionally provoked to anger with insults about their intelligence, way of dressing and general appearance. Under the guise of a wine-tasting test, it was found that those who had no chance to "retaliate" drank significantly more. Imagine the effect on someone who learned in early childhood to *never* be angry. Without even the internal experience of anger, "retaliation" or even response, is impossible. Imagine the effect on drinking in daily life.

Another experiment with "heavy social drinkers" tested whether fear of being evaluated led to increased drinking.[147] Sixty-four male college students participated under the guise of a wine-tasting experiment. Thirty-two were led to believe they would be in a second experiment where they would be *personally* evaluated by a group of women. Needless to say, for a young college man this tended to be a rather intimidating prospect. Those who expected the evaluation drank considerably more than the other group.

In everyday life, people are constantly evaluated when meeting new acquaintances, applying for a job or on a first date. Imagine the intense fear generated and the corresponding increase in alcohol consumption of someone who has been taught, and is "keeping the secret," that they are basically "unfit for survival," "unlovable" and "inherently defective."

A review of the literature on expectancy and drinking behavior[148] cites studies dating back to 1945 about the use of alcohol in relation to issues of personal power. The

---

*"Heavy social drinkers" was defined by dividing college students into five groups depending on the amount they drank. The heavy social drinkers were the top twenty percent in consumption.

studies show that alcohol consumption increases in situations where a person feels powerless or incapable. In our culture, people often expect and therefore often experience, a feeling of power or control when drinking. For someone who's life is pervaded with learned helplessness and is in a constant battle to keep feelings of powerlessness out of awareness, alcohol has great attraction.

Problem drinkers don't consider emotions a helpful source of information. It would be unusual for an alcoholic to appreciate his feelings of sadness, loneliness, anger or helplessness. Even if he should get a glimpse of the meaning and purpose behind them, having learned he is helpless in important areas of his life, he is unlikely to work to solve the problem behind those feelings. Instead, he takes direct action to make the feelings go away. Alcohol is a "useful tool" in this endeavor.

For those who have problems with intimacy, alcohol has much to offer in terms of image if not in substance. Alcohol sales campaigns often associate alcohol with "good times" and "warm intimacy." The alcoholic beverage industry sells its product in advertisements which usually feature either a couple in a romantic setting or a larger group of people enjoying "good times and friendship." People who drink are never, of course, portrayed as lonely social misfits. Our cultural association of alcohol with both sexual and emotional intimacy and enjoyable social interaction is not lost on the alcoholic.

Normally, someone who later becomes a "problem drinker" begins and maintains drinking on a predominately "social" level for years. The problem develops gradually. For the person whose self-hatred allows only shallow interaction with other people, the image of alcohol becomes confused with the reality of intimacy. As frustration increases over the inability to fill human needs for emotionally fulfilling relationships, alcohol offers itself as a symbolic substitute. People who give up excessive drinking or drug use often describe it in terms of giving up a lover or best friend.

Heavy drinking can be seen as an attempt to be good in early childhood terms. Its main physiological effect, the disruption of mental function with a resultant decrease in both self and general awareness, matches many problem drinkers' early childhood lessons of how he should be.

Cultural beliefs about alcohol build the expectancy that alcohol has magical powers to cause behavior totally separate from a person's identity. This allows a person to engage in behaviors that would normally be restrained as contradictory to self-image. This dual attraction of heavy drinking can become an ever-more-attractive solution to life.

As use increases, real problems tend to get worse. As problems get worse, the subconscious struggles harder for attention, meaning it works to generate more intense emotion. If the *subconscious* learns the solution to problems is to drink, what is *perceived as an alien force* begins to impel a person to ever more self-destructive drinking.

There is nothing irrevocable about the addiction process. Tens of millions have quit smoking, a large percentage of overweight people have managed to attain and maintain a desired weight and an estimated two or three percent of alcoholics "go into remission" every year. The reason for these changes varies with the person. Younger substance abusers generally give up their habits as they grow older. It is seen as inconsistent with an adult role as husband or wife and father or mother.

Often, altered circumstances lead to the change. Someone who drinks due to frustration over not being able to find suitable work may promptly moderate upon finding a new job. Someone who drinks due to the loss of a spouse through death or divorce may moderate or quit when they begin to date. Often alcoholics will quit or moderate when they develop a physical intolerance to drinking. It is extremely difficult to keep up a pattern of heavy drinking if the first drink causes sharp stomach pains and the second one makes things worse.

A deep awareness that drinking is not the best choice is what precipitates change. It can take many forms from one morning looking in the mirror and thinking "Why am I doing this? This is not what I want to do," to waking up in a hospital after an accidental overdose and becoming aware that, "I will die if I continue this way."

The deep awareness which often precipitates a change in drinking patterns takes two general forms; a moment of clarity or a painful emotional ordeal. AA members aptly use the term "hitting bottom" to describe the tumultuous emotional ordeal precipitating a desire to change. The "moment of clarity" is often cast in "spiritual" terms and ascribed to an awareness of AA's Higher Power.

These deep awarenesses must be distinguished from "shallow" ones. A conscious, surface decision to change that doesn't reach to the depth of the subconscious *decisions to drink* will leave them unaffected and the drinking behavior "on automatic." A person who internally experiences an inability to stop drinking may be out of touch with the reasons he drinks, have learned he is helpless so his subconscious automatically fails to muster resources for the effort or use "not being able to stop" as a way of protecting his self-image from the knowledge that he *wants to drink*.

However the decision to change develops and is experienced, it may be only the beginning of a protracted process. The addicted person has the job of finding new ways of filling, or trying to fill, his needs. This often takes the form of substituting other addictions. With the blessings, assistance and encouragement of their psychiatrists, drinkers often substitute Valium, Xanax or other anti-anxiety drugs for the alcohol. Abstinent alcoholics often smoke more cigarettes and drink more coffee. Religious or sexual addictions are often substituted or come to the forefront.

Most people who have drinking problems want to moderate their drinking rather than quit altogether. Disease theorists and AA members consider this to be a symptom of the disease, "denial." While there may be a lot of denial on the subject of controlled drinking, the denial seems to be more a characteristic of the disease theorists and AA members. The truth of the matter is that, even after treatment that *works to sabotage the ability to moderate*, almost three times as many alcoholics *do* manage to moderate their drinking as manage to abstain.[149]

Treatment sabotages the ability to moderate by instilling AA's "One drink, one drunk" belief in those who already have drinking problems.[150] This is *teaching learned helplessness*. When people *learn* they can't help but continue drinking, the subconscious automatically fails to marshall the resources to stop. Also, if someone *wants to* get drunk they can "accidentally" or "unwittingly" eat rum cake, use mouthwash or take a sip out of the "wrong glass." By placing the blame on the alcohol and "innocent action," an "alcoholic" *gets to* get drunk *and* preserve his self-image. The alcohol is responsible, not the person.

Some excellent studies have compared the benefits of abstinence and "controlled drinking" as goals of treatment. One of these[151] involved 70 alcoholics who, in order to qualify for the study, must have met certain conditions. They must not have been AA members, must not have believed in the disease theory and must not have been able to manage an extended period of abstinence. The seventy were randomly assigned to one of two groups; one with the goal of abstinence, the other with the goal of moderation. After treatment they were followed for two years. The findings strongly support moderation as a goal over abstinence.

Most of those assigned to the abstinence group objected to the goal. During treatment, *those assigned to abstinence drank more* than those in the controlled drinking group. During the two year follow-up, both groups drank the same in both quantity and frequency. An important point is that most of those assigned to abstinence moderated on their own. Perhaps most important is that while those who were classified as "lighter" drinkers did equally as well in both groups, *those classified as "heavier" drinkers did better with controlled drinking treatment.*

Of course, abstinence is necessary for some people. People with health problems such as liver damage and diabetes must abstain. This is not because one drink inevitably leads to the next but because one drink is injurious to an already ailing body. Abstinence is also clearly necessary for those who *believe* "One drink, one drunk," because for those who *believe* it, one drink, or perhaps even using mouthwash, does lead to one drunk.

This discussion of the merits of abstinence is *not* intended to suggest that people who are successfully abstaining should drink. The point is that for *most* problem drinkers, abstinence is an unrealistic goal. The "loss of control" hypothesis used to support a need for abstinence for "alcoholics" has been proved untrue. The person with drinking problems who wants to moderate his drinking, and hasn't been convinced he can't, in all likelihood will succeed. The situation is entirely different for people with heavy exposure to AA. They almost never moderate. As a matter of fact, *practicing AA's "spiritual principles" usually makes the underlying problems of alcoholics and addicts much worse...*

Chapter 9

Meetings

AA meetings are held in a wide variety of locations. Rooms are rented from churches, schools and community organizations. Treatment centers often give free space. In most cities, AA members, separate from AA itself, band together to establish "clubhouses"; storefronts or houses used exclusively for Twelve Step meetings and socialization by the groupers.

The membership of different groups varies widely. The most readily observable differences are social and economic status and age. In wealthier neighborhoods, of course, the membership is wealthier, in poor neighborhoods, poorer. There are also many exclusive meetings in private homes where an invitation is necessary and "undesirables," however they may be defined, are not invited.

The size of the meetings also varies tremendously, from perhaps half a dozen groupers to hundreds. The larger and more prestigious meetings consistently have speakers with twenty or more years of Time. In Los Angeles, celebrities also lend prestige and the amount of Time they have is of less importance than their celebrity status.

A more prestigious meeting tends to take on the atmosphere of a great crusade. Members of the cheerful crowd greet each other with hugs and pleasantries, exchange bits of gossip about other members, discuss other meetings and share anticipation of the speaker's message. In keeping with the traditions of the Oxford Group, everyone is on a first name basis. Larger meetings normally have one or two speakers who give their "pitch." Sometimes, one-speaker meetings open the floor to questions on the Program for the speaker who, having Time, acts as authority.

Most meetings are smaller; usually substantially less than one-hundred people. They usually open up to "sharing" for witness and confession by individual groupers after the speaker, exactly as was done at Oxford Group meetings. This "Gospel of Personal Experience," whether done by just one elder or by the participation of as many groupers as time allows, is the core of all meetings.

Also part of every meeting is the reading of sacred text. Oxford group, being "more spiritual than religious" used the Bible for readings. Alcoholics Anonymous, being "spiritual not religious," doesn't use the Bible at all but the inspired Word of God as expressed through Bill Wilson; the Big Book provides the sacred text[*].

The Twelve Steps are read at almost every meeting. When taking collection, called "The Seventh Tradition," the Twelve Traditions are read, bringing a spiritual context to the collection of money.

Among the most popular readings is an abbreviated version of Chapter Five from the Big Book. In it, the recovery program of AA is laid out, beginning with "Rarely have we seen a person fail who has thoroughly followed our path...," through the Twelve Steps, and

---

[*]AA members never *say* "the inspired Word of God." They *do* however, *say and believe* that the AA Program and literature were "inspired by God." The present-day grouper may be disturbed at the suggestion that the Big Book is a sacred text but he would likely be horrified if someone were to show irreverence for it.

ending with AA's description of the predicament of the alcoholic and the solution to his problems:

> "(a) That we were alcoholic and could not manage our own lives.
> (b) That probably no human power could have relieved our alcoholism.
> (c) That God could and would if He were sought."[152]

In continuing the traditions of the Oxford Group, AA uses elders as preachers. The quality of the speakers varies but almost anyone with more than a few months Time is a passable if not excellent speaker, able to "carry the message" skillfully with sincerity, passion and humor. Better speakers tend to have the worst "bottoms," both emotionally and behaviorally. Having the worst bottoms, they are living testimonials to the great recovery available to anyone through AA.

To hear the "best" speakers it is usually necessary to go to the more prestigious meetings. Since so few groupers manage to attain 10, 20 or 30 years of "sobriety," people with a great deal of Time are in great demand. In the competition for speakers, the larger, more prestigious meetings usually win out.

The speech itself is called "sharing," just as in the Oxford Group. It is Oxford Group's "Gospel of Personal Experience" although it is now called "sharing personal experience," "Twelfth Step sharing," or "sharing experience, strength, and hope."

This sharing, more aptly called a sermon, begins with the telling of immorality, misery and ruination at the hands of Devil Drink, now referred to as alcohol or alcoholism. It goes on to tell of "spiritual awakening" in AA. Unlike Oxford Group, which attributed salvation and redemption by Jesus through the Oxford Group*, AA proclaims "recovery" by one's "Higher Power" through the Twelve Steps and Alcoholics Anonymous. The general format for the sermon is, "What it was like then, how I got here and what it is like now." In order to "not preach," the speaker carefully restricts use of the word "you." Almost everything is said in terms of "I," "we" and "alcoholics."

The speaker opens the sermon by identifying himself by his first name and "disease" or "diseases." The diseases are usually defined as such by the existence of Twelve Step programs to "recover" from them. For instance, "My name is John and I'm an alcoholic and a junkie." Using only the first name is thought to protect anonymity and maintain humility. Labeling oneself as "alcoholic," with or without other diseases, is considered essential for beginners to help break through "denial" and establish humility. It is also considered essential in maintaining recovery because, unless humility is maintained, God will not protect the alcoholic from Devil Drink.

After identifying himself, the speaker may tell a joke on himself or alcoholics in general to warm up the audience before beginning with "what it was like." He recites his past in terms of the "disease" of alcoholism. The word sin is never used, but it is hardly a medical history as might seem appropriate to those who only know of alcoholism through *public* statements of people "in recovery" and treatment industry advertising. The word "sin" is replaced with "defects of character." Unlike

---

*Evidently the Bible, and Jesus along with it, were discardable even before the rise of Alcoholics Anonymous. It was reported that in India in the 1920s and '30s, where local religious groups were offended by attempts at conversion to Christianity, groupers also dropped Jesus in order to more effectively win converts to their organization.

the Oxford Group members, who confessed to having been "wretched" or "lost" sinners, today's AA groupers confess to having been "sick," "suffering" or "drinking" alcoholics.

The main theme of this part of the sermon is the confession (called "admitting" in AA) of "defectiveness" and "powerlessness" "from the beginning." Confession of the worst sins are usually made with little sadness, guilt or penance attached and often in a joking, sensationalistic manner.* The confession of sins may begin in childhood or with the first drink.

Sins of childhood generally cover three main areas; physical, emotional and spiritual, since alcoholism is considered a physical, emotional and spiritual disease. The physical aspect of the disease can include symptoms of "alcoholic thinking" and "reacting wrong" before ever having had a drink. For instance, I remember one speaker who told of being punished as an eleven-year-old for making a B on his report card instead of his customary straight A's. He was grounded and forced to stay in his bedroom for the next semester. He then told how he reacted wrong; he became rebellious.

Any childhood misbehavior is held up as a symptom of disease. Another speaker shared a rather popular theme. As a child, he thought he was adopted even though he wasn't. Among the emotional symptoms of the disease in childhood are having felt lonely, sad, angry and different; as though one didn't belong. These "symptoms" are described in the context of "abnormal" or "alcoholic" sensitivity as Bill Wilson described his despair as a child at being abandoned by his father to his mentally-ill,

---

*This refers only to the main speaker. Other groupers may later share for confession, called "Fifth Step sharing" which, in stark contrast to "Twelfth Step sharing" is normally characterized by a penitent attitude and remorse.

abusive mother.

While AA attributes all "character defects" to "not working a spiritual program," AA spirituality is usually mentioned to newcomers in only the broadest terms.

Often, the speaker will tell a story about himself to prove that he has always been defective. This may be at the time of the first drink ever taken but often predates it. One man shared that, when he was sixteen, a girl he had been going with for a year broke up with him. "I felt abandoned," and he continued, "I've always been that way." Another speaker told how she always had behavior problems. At two and a half, she would lay awake at night. "My father was a psychiatrist so I know it wasn't anything my parents did." She knew she was defective from the start. Earlier, however, she had shared that her grandmother died when she was two and a half. Her wise parents told her Grandma was asleep; they didn't want to upset her. When speaking of themselves in childhood, AA members *always* describe themselves, with all sincerity, as "bad."

The portion of the sermon which begins with the first drink ever taken and ends with finding AA is called the "drunk-a-log." Sermons often begin here and often it is almost the entire sermon. It is here, beginning with the first drink, that the speaker "qualifies." To "qualify" means to prove one's authority, wisdom and right to preach to others by telling how incompetent one has been with respect to alcohol. Usually beginning with, "I drank alcoholicly from the start," the speaker tells of loss of control over both drinking and behavior. Except for the seriousness with which the concept is held, the overall message is reminiscent of Flip Wilson's comic character Geraldine saying, "The Devil made me do it." The greater the "sins" committed while under the influence of Devil Drink, the more appreciation the congregation of groupers shows for the speaker. The speaker confirms for them the Powerlessness of an "alcoholic" in the face of the "cunning, baffling, and powerful" disease of alcoholism.

In speaking of the individual symptoms of the disease, the speaker offers specific characteristics of alcoholics which vary somewhat from speaker to speaker. Among ones which may be heard are, "I thought it was cool to drink." "I feel euphoric when I drink; alcoholics are different." "I was angry at the world."

Whatever the particular symptoms given, the speaker paints everything in his past, prior to AA, in terms of "unmanageability," hopelessness, desperation and "disease." All pre-AA hopes, dreams, emotion and thought are now recognized to have been the result of "the disease."

To prove their powerlessness, speakers usually admit to futile attempts to stop drinking "alone," meaning without AA. Jokes are made about their personal experience of the futility of various therapies. Speakers ridicule themselves for any attempts to stop drinking without AA even if they succeeded for months or years longer than they have in AA. They also ridicule themselves for not admitting their disease and its "true nature," meaning their own Powerlessness.

This is often the point where impassioned pleas are made to the newcomer. "Alcoholics rarely recover on their own." The speaker may then point to the Twelve Steps posted on the wall. "Look, this is a 'we' program, not an 'I' program. You don't have to do it alone. Let us love you until you learn to love yourself."

The first-timer at a meeting may be awed by the sincerity, "honesty" and telling of intimate secrets. This is a direct result of the "humility" of the speaker as expressed through his admission of the "unmanageability" of his life before AA and his "powerlessness" in the face of alcoholism. The theme is expanded in clichés like, "My best thinking got me here," and "I am my own worst enemy." The speaker will often admit his motivation for "working with others," including speaking, is to "stay sober myself." The speaker never suggests there are good qualities within himself. All good flows from the Program.

The "how I got here" portion of the sermon maintains the humility of the speaker. First time attendees attribute their presence to a variety of reasons: court order, "intervention," or a friend's suggestion, among others. Even highly religious persons attribute their arrival to a variety of reasons. The person with Time, however, has always been guided by the direct intervention of God. God got them arrested, had their family intervene or sent an "Eskimo" (an AA elder)* to "bring me in from the cold." Never, ever, have I heard an AA speaker say anything remotely resembling, "I thought I had a problem so I used the brains God gave me and sought help." The speaker is likely, with all due humility, to instead announce, "I thought. Ha! Ha!" to which the groupers respond with knowing laughter.

The "what it is like now" portion of the sermon is an expression of gratitude toward AA and a demonstration of recovery in AA. This portion usually stresses the sincerely held belief that, "AA saved my life." Examples are often given of people who, not having found the Program or not having stayed in the Program, eventually drank themselves to death. The speaker holds himself up as someone saved from inevitable "jails, institutions, and death" by Alcoholics Anonymous. Since AA rescued the

---

*The term "Eskimo" can also refer to any person involved in a "coincidence" arranged by God which leads a person to AA. AA members, like the Oxford Groupers before them, believe "there are no coincidences" and they should constantly be on the lookout for what appear to be coincidences because they are clues to God's will.

drinking alcoholic from the clutches of Devil Drink, anything now perceived as good in the speaker's life is directly attributed to the Program, since without AA the speaker wouldn't even be alive. "I owe my life to Alcoholics Anonymous."

The speaker goes into detail about the benefits received by working the steps. Among the most important and frequently cited is the finding of Serenity. Serenity, as portrayed by the speaker, is not suffering from the feelings presumably experienced only by the drinking alcoholic. It is usually described as a state of "evenness." This evenness is due to no longer feeling resentments (anger) and self-pity (sadness, loneliness, or hopelessness). It also includes not feeling extremes of happiness, or "too" good. The only human emotion that seems consistent with Serenity is Gratitude. This state is referred to as "utopia" in the Big Book.*

The speaker will tell how serenity is maintained "One day at a time" by working the Steps. He will perhaps give examples of how his serenity was temporarily lost or endangered by allowing an evil internal force (personalized as "My alcoholic told me...") to come between himself and his Higher Power.

If the speaker has told of "not being understood" in his "suffering alcoholic" days, he will now tell of the understanding found in AA. "I never felt I was understood. I didn't know I was an alcoholic. Normies can't understand an alcoholic. Only another alcoholic can understand."

Related to "being understood" is "belonging." "I never felt like I belonged. I belong here. I am an alcoholic." The speaker may tell of the love found in AA and de-

---

*"Utopia" originally was worded "heaven on earth." It was changed prior to publication in order to not be overtly contradictory to Catholic beliefs. *Pass It On*, p. 201

scribe AA as "my real family." Among the loving acts attributed to AA is "They loved me enough to tell me the truth." This is another point where the speaker may implore the newcomer to "Let us love you until you learn to love yourself." Evidence of how the speaker has learned to love himself is often expressed by "I get on my knees every morning and admit my powerlessness," "I work the Steps," and "I force myself to go to meetings even when I don't want to."

There is a sharp dividing line between what is "good" and what is "bad" in AA. Everything good in life is attributed to "working a Spiritual Program." Everything "bad," such as emotions other than Gratitude, troubling thoughts, and wanting to drink are attributed, in part, to the "alcoholic self," not following direction (Oxford Group's Guidance) from God, one's sponsor and other elders, not attending enough meetings, forgetting one's own Powerlessness, not working the Steps, and not "working with others."

The "what it is like now" portion of the sermon can be summarized as "No matter how 'bad' you are and have been, I was worse and AA keeps me 'good.' I don't feel pain. You can be good and not feel pain too."

The speaker models being good in many ways. He doesn't show "bad" feelings, instead displaying Gratitude, Serenity and good cheer. When speaking of past trauma, instead of expressing the feelings normally associated with tragedy, he will laugh at himself and often invites the other groupers to join in with a self-disparaging joke. Laughing at his own pain and inviting others to join in allows him to demonstrate how he has "recovered" in the Program.

The congregation assists the good speaker with unanimous responses to the clichés and other ultimate truths. They don't often shout "Amen," but rather shout "right on" and "yeah," nod in agreement and burst into applause or laughter at the appropriate moments. This is not to suggest that the groupers consciously work together to respond in a particular fashion but that they all hold the same beliefs and view things from a similar perspective. If a speaker tells a joke about how he "thought," all the groupers, *knowing* how alcoholics suffer from "alcoholic thinking," are compelled to laugh along. A speaker may tell of a tragedy that befell him because he didn't take the first step seriously enough. Everyone *knows* what happens when powerlessness is not admitted, so they can nod in agreement. When a speaker says, "When I'm alone with myself I'm behind enemy lines," the groupers can all relate and laugh along because they know what it is like to be alone with themselves.

Speakers find it important to give certain warnings to the newcomer. These are consistent with the presumed three major components of alcoholism as a physical, emotional and spiritual disease. Under the physical attributes falls the presumed uncontrollable craving that develops after the first drink or perhaps just a sip. The warning clichés are, "One drink, one drunk," and "Don't drink or use no matter what."

Another area, which could be attributed to either the physical or emotional aspect of the disease, is "alcoholic thinking." Symptoms that the newcomer is cautioned to watch out for (dangerous thoughts) are: thinking you might not be an alcoholic, thinking you don't need the Program, disagreement with someone with more Time, thinking you don't need a sponsor or thinking that you can stop at one drink. The speaker often uses himself as an example and may give the warning indirectly. "When I was new, they told me I needed to work the first step. I thought I didn't need to. Let me tell you, not everyone makes it back." The speaker may then go on to list AA members who drank themselves to death as a result of not following direction, of not "Surrendering to the

119

Program."

Newcomers are warned against the emotional symptoms of the disease such as feeling angry, sad, lonely or afraid. These feeling are all ways that "cunning, baffling, and powerful" alcohol impels an alcoholic, against his will, to take the first drink. The speaker may say, "I can't afford to be angry anymore," or "Resentment is the number one reason for slipping." Sadness, loneliness and hopelessness, grouped together as self-pity or "being on the pity pot," are also symptoms of alcoholism and tricks used by "my alcoholic" (the "Evil One" of Oxford Group) to "lead me to the first drink." According to the Big Book, "Sometimes we think fear ought to be classed with stealing. It seems to cause more trouble."[153] A speaker may caution the newcomer with, "F.E.A.R.: False Evidence Appearing Real."

"Spirituality" is generally treated rather lightly at newcomer meetings because, as the Big Book cautions, "There is no use arousing any prejudice he [the pigeon] may have against certain theological terms and conceptions about which he may already be confused."[154]

One of the most popular clichés which gives a warning of a spiritual nature is, "Don't leave five minutes before the miracle," meaning that Serenity is just around the corner. Also of a spiritual nature, although they may not be presented that way, are warnings of what happens when one doesn't admit one's disease, doesn't work the Steps or doesn't get a sponsor.

The warnings and aims of a newcomer's meeting are well summed up by one of the more popular clichés, "H.A.L.T.: Don't get too Hungry, Angry, Lonely, or Tired." All four are considered to put an alcoholic at risk of taking the first drink. Hunger and tiredness can be attended to by the newcomer himself but anger and loneliness are emotional symptoms of a spiritual disease which need spiritual attention. The newcomer is cautioned to either telephone an AA member or go to a meeting at the first sign of a bad emotion or wanting to drink. Going to meetings and getting direction from an Elder are both considered spiritual in AA even if they are not presented to the newcomer as spiritual principles.

Little direct advice is normally given at a newcomer meeting but what is given is presented carefully. The most important step in rescuing the "still suffering alcoholic" is to get them to commit to attending more meetings. The only direct advice that may be given can be summed up by the cliché "90 meetings in 90 days." One popular way of expressing this and exhorting the newcomer to return is "Just stick around for 90 days and we will refund your misery." The suggestion may also be of the form "If you are new here, you are too new to know if you need AA, so just go to 90 meetings in 90 days and then you can decide."

Other common suggestions are to begin working the steps, "No one ever drank while working the steps," and to get a sponsor. Those who doubt they have the disease may be encouraged to "Just stop for a year. Only an alcoholic would have a problem with it or object to it."

Meetings often include the ritual of giving "chips" and observing "birthdays." Chips, tokens such as key rings or medallions, are given for "varying lengths of sobriety." The periods observed in this way are 30, 60, 90, and 180 days. Each honored member usually has a few moments to address the congregation. He expresses gratitude to the Program for making it all possible and exhorts those with less Time to "Keep coming back, it really works!"

Following the giving of chips, birthdays are celebrated. It is a joyous occasion complete with cake, candles and the singing of "Happy Birthday" by the entire congregation to observe the achievement of one or more years of continuous abstinence. For the AA member, it is public acknowledgement of "working a good program" and a celebration of AA's most intensely held value, absolute abstinence. The AA birthday supercedes the importance of "natal" birthdays, which must be distinguished in conversation to avoid confusion.

While the AA birthday is a joyous occasion marking spiritual progress, "natal" birthdays are seen as a day when the grouper is in special danger of drinking, as are all holidays celebrated by "normies." Real birthdays, Christmas, Thanksgiving, and New Year's Eve are all days in which one is particularly vulnerable to Devil Drink. One is warned that, at these times, it is wise to stay particularly close to the Program. To this end, marathon, twenty-four-hour meetings are held on holidays.

Most meetings open the floor for witnessing and confession from the congregation. New groupers, with only days, weeks or months of Time, engage in Oxford Group's "sharing for confession," now called "Fifth Step sharing." These confessions, known as "being honest" and "admitting defects of character" are, in contrast to the Twelfth Step sharing of the speaker, usually highly charged with anger, sadness and remorse. Among the most emotional confessions are those of someone who has had a drink of alcohol. The penitent will share his realization of Powerlessness and express great Humility. Humility and self-humiliation are always cheerfully applauded by AA members. These are qualities at the heart of AA spirituality and are held as essential to maintaining recovery.[*]

If the sharer deviates from AA doctrine, the audience

---

[*]To quote an "early and wonderful friend of AA," "Alcoholics Anonymous is natural; it is natural at the point where nature comes closest to the supernatural, namely in humiliations and in consequent humility." — Big Book p. 574

may respond with derisive laughter, boos, stony silence, patronization or expressions of fear for the sharer. Groupers with more Time will "help" the novice. For instance, if someone with three months Time should announce that he has stayed sober without working the steps, an Elder (someone with more than three months) may share how the Steps are but suggestions and no one has to work them if they don't want to. He will then go on to list all the pitiful examples of those who drank themselves to death because "their disease told them" they didn't need to work the Steps.

Groupers with Time are interspersed with "beginners." Those with Time share in the same fashion as the speaker, often thanking the speaker for his wise words and, perhaps, testifying to the speaker's "having good sobriety." They will also give their own abbreviated version of "What it was like then and what it is like now," witnessing to their own miraculous recovery in AA.

There is no sharp dividing line between those who engage in sharing for witness and those who share for confession. A sharer may first make a tearful confession then follow it with praise for the Program. Nor is a great deal of Time necessary to engage in Twelfth Step sharing. The difference is determined by a grouper's relative status in a meeting. In a treatment center, for example, perhaps no one has even thirty days of abstinence. Under these circumstances, those with the most Time, even if only two or three weeks, tend to take on the role of elder authority and witness to the success of the AA-based treatment and the wisdom of AA. They will also point out errors in thought and dispense advice to those with less Time.

One thing clear to the casual observer is the recovery evident in those with Time. They can laugh at things the newer grouper cries about. They have licked the alcohol problem and their good cheer and Serenity bear witness to the difference between themselves and those who have only begun in AA.

At the end of the meeting, someone is chosen to lead the closing prayer. This is usually the Lord's Prayer but may be the Serenity Prayer. At the close of the prayer, the members all chant with conviction, "Keep coming back, it really works!" This is the end of the meeting but may not be the end of the meeting experience. Groupers get together for coffee afterwards and the newcomer is invited.

For the newcomer, much that the speaker says resonates at a very deep level within him. Whether he arrives under his own volition or court order, or even if he has already moderated or stopped drinking, he is in an extremely vulnerable position. The crutch, alcohol, which has been used for so long to reduce awareness of emotions, drown out the ability to think or as a defense against attributing real or imagined misbehavior to himself, is not, at the moment, a viable alternative.

When the speaker and other sharers tell about "what it was like," the newcomer can relate to the feelings they suffered from prior to AA. Without alcohol to dull mental function, he is likely to be fighting off overwhelming feelings of anger, sadness, loneliness and "badness."

It is not surprising that someone who has learned to automatically suppress self-awareness would be at a loss to explain, even to himself, not only excessive drinking, but any of his behavior. When he hears of the "Powerlessness" and "unmanageability" of alcoholics, that they are victims of a disease, it rings true. His subjective experience is that his drinking comes from somewhere outside himself and lessons of learned helplessness carried forward from childhood leave him with a feeling of powerlessness.

Other characteristics of "drinking alcoholics" described

at AA meetings are likely to hit home with the newcomer. Anyone whose self-hatred is so intense that he seeks to drown normal mental functioning and self-awareness feels unloved. By the same token, the newcomer to AA is likely to feel misunderstood. His self-awareness is extremely limited. The problem is not so much an inability of others to understand but an inability to understand and express himself. For instance, imagine that a problem drinker goes on a binge every time his feelings are hurt. The problem drinker may insist, especially to himself, that his feelings were not hurt. The drinking helps him be "not aware." If the drinker has achieved his aim of "not being aware" by drinking, he would be unaware of his feelings having been hurt. Any suggestion by someone who actually does understand the situation that his feelings were indeed hurt would *prove to him* he wasn't understood.

The newcomer is also likely to feel different from others. Having learned in early childhood that essential parts of his personality are bad and not to be acknowledged, he never has the opportunity to learn that other people have similar feelings and thoughts, or at least would have if they had suffered a similar situation. In AA, these feelings of being different are familiar to all. They are a symptom of "the disease."

The AA environment is a recreation of the addictive family system. The "bad" presented in an AA meeting is the same "bad" taught children in an addictive family system. One's awareness, emotions and thinking are presented as symptoms of a disease. The ideal modeled by the speaker and other elders is the ideal taught to children in addictive family systems. The AA value of Serenity, an emotional void fillable only with Gratitude, closely matches childhood's lessons of don't be angry, sad, afraid, lonely or "too happy." Those "in recovery" present themselves to newcomers as having achieved this drug-like state of Serenity. It can be termed drug-like, because drugs are the most efficient and popular way of suppressing normal human emotion.

The speaker also models the ideals taught in the addictive family system by discounting his own thinking. The child wasn't ridiculed or punished for agreeing with his parents but for having "bad thoughts" or, better stated, questioning his parents' statements, actions or attitudes. The speaker is a "good child." He discounts his own thoughts.

One very attractive concept for the newcomer is that, unlike in the past where he could only blame alcohol for behavior when actually drinking, with AA's disease of alcoholism, he can attribute everything troubling within himself to alcohol. Every feeling, thought, act or shortcoming which he deems "bad" is merely a disease symptom. This even includes before he has ever taken a drink. For example, if he still feels guilty about poor grades in school, even if he didn't have his first drink until after graduation, he can now blame alcoholism. He is "good" and "innocent." He is a victim of a disease. He is also in a room full of people who are in unanimous agreement. They agree because they "understand."

There is a great deal promised to the newcomer. The most clearly and overtly made promise is that "It really works." This means the newcomer will be able to share the solution found by others to the "alcohol problem" who were, according to their pitches, usually far worse off than the newcomer.

Perhaps the most attractive promise is the Serenity claimed and modeled by the AA elders. According to their statements and demeanor at meetings, they avoid or quickly dispose of "resentment" and "self-pity." They can, rather than feel pain, laugh at the most painful of experiences. Due to their Spiritual Program, they are above normal human emotion.

The newcomer is not necessarily overwhelmed by the meeting nor is he necessarily enthused about attending again. The only important point from the perspective of cult recruitment is that he does attend again, perhaps even making a commitment to attend 90 meetings in 90 days until he is "qualified" to decide whether he needs AA or not.

The first time visitor is often overwhelmed. He may find it extremely difficult to remain unmoved by what he has seen and heard. In the space of an hour or two, stories of wrecked and healed lives are presented. Newer members pour out their anguished hearts and souls. The audience may be moved in quick succession from sadness, to anger, to joy, to gratitude. Wild applause and laughter echos from the walls. The newcomer may leave his first encounter with the impression that the groupers, in spite of holding some odd beliefs and using rather cryptic language, are extremely sincere, open, happy and have found something that "really works." But this is only a small part of the dynamics of a meeting. The more important, *life-changing* effects of the meeting are much more subtle.

The most important part of recruitment in any mind-control cult is meeting attendance. One of the reasons for this is well demonstrated in a series of classic experiments done in the early 1950s by Solomon Asch.[155]

Various numbers of people in a room were given the job of determining which of two lines was longest even though one was obviously longer than the other. Each participant gave his answer in turn. This would be repeated several times. The catch was that all but the last to announce were confederates of the experimenter. They would all either give the right answer or all give the wrong answer. The purpose of the experiments were to determine the effect on the last person.

Only one in four of the subjects managed to remain independent and give the correct answer every time, even though the answer was obvious. Some of those who answered incorrectly were "just going along," but some actually believed the obviously incorrect answers they gave were correct. *Every one of them, even the ones who managed to stay independent, began to doubt their own perceptions.*

The effect of the majority's unanimity was *to create distrust of one's own perception.* In the vast majority of cases it also changed the subject's behavior. In the more extreme cases, it actually altered the person's perceptions.

In everyday life, this can be considered to have little lasting effect. A Jewish person attending a Methodist church service will be confronted with many unanimous opinions directly contradicting his own. He may even wonder, for a moment, whether Jesus is the real Messiah but he is extremely unlikely to change his beliefs. He ultimately trusts his own life, his own thought processes and his own conclusions.

The situation is entirely different in a cult meeting. One of the major differences between legitimate organizations and mind-control cults is that, in cults, one of the unanimous opinions is that the potential new member is incapable of exercising good judgement. Any disagreement or disbelief of doctrine is treated as a sign of that poor judgement. In AA, this is expressed as "alcoholic thinking" and "haven't been around long enough to know." It is also expressed in patronizing attitudes.

This attitude is also reflected in the names that members use to describe targets of indoctrination. Scientologists refer to them as "raw meat." Oxford Group referred to them as "lost sheep." Alcoholics Anonymous refers to them as "pigeons," "beginners" and "babies." Of course, all these terms are used lovingly.

Being a minority of one is far from the only factor which influences the potential recruit. Further explanation of cult mind-control techniques calls for the use of a slightly expanded version of the model of the mind used in Chapter Five. As was discussed, the human mind is of two parts, the conscious and the subconscious. The conscious mind processes information and sends it to the subconscious for storage and later reference. One part of the conscious mind, which here will be called the "critical factor," is responsible for critically interpreting information before it is stored in the subconscious for later use.

Imagine again a Jewish man at a Christian church service. He is likely to hear statements and phrases expressed in either the sermon or in the singing of hymns such as "Jesus is our Lord and Savior," and "Jesus lives." Statements about Jesus will be analyzed by the critical factor against ideas already held in the subconscious. They will be found to be not self-relevant, to be other people's beliefs, and will be stored as such. Just hearing the word Jesus would be a tip-off that the information being received was about *someone else's* religion. Statements about Jesus would be stored for later recall as fact, not about his own reality, but about Christian belief. There is little or no chance that he would be converted to Christianity.

Of course, the response of a Christian in a Jewish service would be identical. The information would be critically analyzed and stored in the subconscious, not as one's own reality, but as information about Jewish beliefs and practices.

Now, imagine for a moment a person with no "critical factor." He would store every piece of information *unquestioningly* in his subconscious as a "bottom line" truth. After leaving a Christian service he'd be Christian. The next day, if he were to go to a Jewish service, he'd leave with the Jewish faith. Witnessing a political debate, he would switch sides as quickly and often as the speakers changed. Every statement would be accepted uncritically. When he "went to check" his beliefs, he would find someone else's beliefs *in place of* his own. He wouldn't even recognize them as "not his." Thinking they are his, which carries the "automatic" implication they are true, they are beyond questioning.

Of course, no one is so suggestible. Everyone has a "critical factor" which filters and processes information for storage. The important point for cult recruitment is to bypass the critical factor, the ability to analyze and alter information before storage in the subconscious. In Alcoholics Anonymous meetings, this is done in various ways. Combined with the effect of being "a minority of one" these methods can have profound effects on the personality.

One of the ways the critical factor is bypassed is in the "humility" of the speaker. People are rightly a little suspicious of others who claim to be doing "good deeds" expecting nothing in return. The AA speaker quickly lays this suspicion to rest; "I am doing this to stay sober myself." There is never any hint that this is not true. Body language proves the sincerity of the speaker. The simple statement of the speaker carries several implications which may bypass the critical faculty with acceptance that the speaker is indeed speaking to stay sober. These are, "Speaking at AA meetings keeps people from drinking," "The speaker is abstinent," and "There is no ulterior motivation (and therefore no danger) involved."

When the speaker discounts himself, it has the paradoxical effect of building credibility. It defies reason that someone would confess to terrible misbehavior and personal inadequacy, and then could turn around and give, with absolute sincerity, inaccurate information about "alcoholics" or "recovery" to the unanimous approval and agreement of a room full of people.

One of the popular ways to establish humility is for a speaker to say he is a liar. How is one to analyze what he has to say? He is obviously very sincere. Starting with stating he is a liar, he either is a liar and is now telling the truth, or he normally is not a liar, but is lying now, so he normally tells the truth. There is obviously great truth and meaning in this statement, judging by the unanimous understanding of the groupers. The problem is to find it. One's own credibility is reduced; "I don't understand." The speaker's credibility is increased, "What he is saying must have meaning."

With the speaker's sincerity established through "humility," he is virtually unchallengeable since *he says he is guilty*. Planting thoughts in the pigeon's subconscious becomes much easier.

As done by a skilled hypnotherapist, a skilled AA speaker presents statements in a certain order. A statement which otherwise would be rejected has a much better chance of slipping into the subconscious if it is immediately preceded by two or three unchallengeable statements. For example, a hypnotherapist, while inducing trance may say, "You can feel the weight of your body pressing down against the chair. Take note of your hands, whether they feel warm or cold. Now notice how your breathing is becoming deeper and slower." The first two statements are unchallengeable and the mind is expecting another unchallengeable statement. In the third statement, the instruction to "notice how your breathing is becoming...," normally slips by the critical faculty and the subconscious will act on it. *The client will notice how his breathing is becoming deeper and slower*.

This same method is used by AA speakers. In keeping with proper humility, speakers make some statement about themselves. "I thought I could stop alone." This statement is unchallengeable. Anyone listening would have *no basis* to make a judgement except on the already established sincerity of the speaker. The statement is likely to be followed by, "Alcoholics usually won't admit they can't stop alone." This is also "unchallengeable." The newcomer has little frame of reference for the characteristics of alcoholics in general and must defer to the sincere "authority" and unanimous majority. "If you think you can stop on your own, let me advise you, you don't have to." Again nothing challengeable. The pigeon is now ill prepared to critically analyze any statement. Should the next statement be, "Let us love you until you learn to love yourself," even if a person thinks, "No thanks," several ideas may be planted in the subconscious. "Let us love you" implies that the speaker and other groupers are willing to love the newcomer. It also implies they are capable of loving. Another implication is that with AA, one will learn to love oneself.

One of the most important suggestions implanted this way is done with the ever-popular clichés, "Alcoholics Anonymous requires no beliefs." "The Steps are but suggestions only." The speaker, having made these "unchallengeable" assertions, now will likely tell how a dearly beloved friend died because he didn't work the Steps. The suggestion implanted in the subconscious is not that it is unnecessary to work the Steps, or to believe, but that one will die if he doesn't work the Steps.

Another method of bypassing the critical faculty is the use of double-binds. This is the use of a statement such as; "If this is your first meeting, and you are wondering if you might be alcoholic, let me assure you that you are. You wouldn't be here if you weren't." Another example would be, "If you come into these rooms you belong here. Well, maybe one person in a million doesn't belong here but, if you think you're that person, then you really do belong here." The only way out is to discredit the speaker but the speaker has already established his sincerity by discrediting himself. The only simple, "logical" conclusion is that one is an alcoholic and "belongs here."

At an AA meeting, the tendency is for the newcomer's critical faculty to be overwhelmed by hypnotic suggestion, double-binds, being "a minority of one" and possibly also being in an extremely emotional environment. He is also likely to be in an overwhelming, almost impossible, struggle to understand the language. Everyone speaks in clichés and words seem to have different meanings.

The most complex and most trivial of life's problems are reduced to clichés in mind-control cults. One of the hallmarks of these groups is their cliché-ridden language. Clichés are thought by members to contain great wisdom and ultimate truths and are used to express enduring doctrinal values. However, in spite of the perceived value of the cliché, it short circuits critical judgement and thought. For this reason, the jargon has been called "the language of non-thought."[156]

In AA, a simple statement like, "No one ever drank while working the steps" conveys the concept that working the steps prevents drinking and that the person who has been drinking was at fault. He wasn't working the steps. Of course this statement is about as true as any such simple statement can be. Its truth and wisdom stops further inquiry into the reason for someone's drinking, offers the doctrinal solution for drinking and deflects consideration of any imperfection in AA. Of course, other unused but truer statements might be, "No one ever drank while scuba diving" and "No one ever drank on a space mission."

AA's most popular cliché is "One day at a time." While this is presented to the public as nothing more than a core belief about AA's method of maintaining abstinence "one day at a time," it also serves much wider purposes. Alcoholics are thought to concern themselves too much with the future and the past. It is a "disease" symptom. For instance, a relative newcomer may question being sick, having to attend meetings and carrying out cult duties for the rest of his life. Of course, this is "alcoholic thinking." To help the newcomer, he is gently reminded, "One day at a time."

The difficulty of early abstention was moderated by taking it "one day at a time," and the experience translates well to other difficulties. No matter how empty or painful life in the group may become, life's problems can be handled "one day at a time." Of course following this cliché wholeheartedly excludes planning for the future or even having a vision of the future. It also makes leaving most unlikely.

Another popular AA cliché, "K.I.S.S.: Keep It Simple Stupid," reminds the grouper that it is stupid to see the complexities of life. This serves a vital purpose. As long as the grouper sees things in the simplest terms, "alcoholic thinking" can never fully take over. "Spiritual growth" is assured. Another way of phrasing this cliché which would have the same meaning in practice would be "You're stupid. Don't even try to think. You're only causing yourself problems."

Other clichés are used to obscure the obvious. The only thing more common among AA members than abstinence is binge drinking. An AA member is constantly confronted with other groupers "slipping," "relapsing" and being "out there." What is most disconcerting is when those with more Time drink. Even those with many years of Time may find this disturbing. The real danger, however, is that someone new, either because of an "alcoholic fog" or "spiritual ignorance," might come to the conclusion that the program doesn't *really* work or at least not really well. Many clichés are used to obscure the reality from newcomers and old-timers alike.

"Keep coming back, it really works," as mentioned

earlier, takes a prominent position in many meetings as an after-prayer chant. In meetings where doubt as to the effectiveness of AA has been vocalized, elder groupers may adlib at the end of the chant, "If you work it!" This affirms the perfection of the program and clears up matters for those who may be confused. People in the program, even if they have been working at it for years, don't drink because of a fault in the program; it is their own fault; they weren't *really* working it.

"I am a miracle" supports the deeply held belief that each day an alcoholic doesn't drink is a miracle performed by God through AA. Drinking is to be expected among those who are "Powerless over alcohol." What one is supposed to consider remarkable is not how often AA members binge but that sometimes some of them don't for many years. All members should be grateful for the time that AA gives them sober.

One particularly insidious cliché, which becomes more true with time, is "Only another alcoholic will understand." As the "loaded language" is adopted, communication with non-members becomes ever more difficult. For instance, if a new AA member manages to abstain for two weeks then drinks over being fired, he will be told, or perhaps has already learned, that, "I drank because I am an alcoholic." No other response is acceptable. While this phrase has great meaning to fellow groupers since it expresses the predicament of an alcoholic at the mercy of Devil Drink, it means virtually nothing to humanity at large. A family member or friend who inquires about the drinking episode, if told "because I am an alcoholic," will have extreme difficulty "understanding." He will perhaps think, "Of course you drank because you are an alcoholic. And an overeater would have overeaten." If he further inquires as to the cause of the drinking, he may be told, "I didn't admit my Powerlessness." Now the family member or friend is entirely lost. He really doesn't understand. The new grouper now understands the wisdom of this cliché. If he wants understanding, he must get it from other AA members.

This is entirely different from what the pre-cult conversation over a drinking binge would have been. The problem drinker would have likely answered "I don't know" or "because I got fired." Of course, neither is a complete answer but some degree of communication and understanding would have been possible. Adopting AA language makes being understood by a "normie" almost impossible.

Loaded language, the language of non-thought, entails more than clichés. Individual words are given meanings or shades of meaning entirely separate from their normal usage. For example:

alcohol — demonic creature from "spiritual" world, great dark force, opposite of spirituality. Only some people are susceptible to its cunning, baffling and powerful effects. Those who are susceptible need a spiritual program or they will either die or be institutionalized for life.

alcoholism — a physical, emotional and spiritual disease. Alcoholism kills. There is no cure. "Once an alcoholic, always an alcoholic." One must work a spiritual program one day at a time to avoid death.

spiritual program — a program of living in accordance with God's plan. Alcoholics must be careful to distinguish it from religious programs which may be very nice but are relatively useless for the alcoholic. Religious programs require beliefs. Spiritual programs are better because they are suggestive only. They only need to be suggested because alcoholics who don't follow them die. As far as can be determined, AA and other Twelve Step programs are the only *really* spiritual ones.

God — supernatural being more powerful than Devil Drink. Giver of the Twelve Steps, a guide to living in accordance with His will. Unlikely to save alcoholics who are too willful to work a spiritual program. All available evidence indicates that God is unlikely to help those whose willfulness causes them to depend on a religious instead of a purely spiritual program.

abstinence — similar to Standard English, refraining from drinking alcohol. This is stricter in AA because mouthwash, breath freshener and freshly-baked bread all contain alcohol. The wise alcoholic in a spiritual program usually avoids all of them. Abstinence is Absolute.

dry drunk — painful state characteristic of alcoholics who abstain without benefit of a spiritual program. Also characteristic of members of a spiritual program who don't take their program seriously enough. A state of insanity similar to that of the drinking alcoholic. One should be careful to note that no matter how happy, well-adjusted and successful those without the program may seem they are really just "whistling in the dark." They don't have a program.

sobriety — a special state of Grace gained by working the Steps and maintaining absolute abstinence. It is characterized by feelings of Serenity and Gratitude. It is a state of living according to God's will, not one's own. It is sanity.

These meanings are not usually directly presented to the newcomer and may not ever be directly stated. For example, no grouper would ever refer to alcohol as a "demonic creature." It is just treated as such. A grouper will tell of *what alcohol did to him*, not what *his use of alcohol did to him*. Alcohol, a liquid that is no more capable of thought or *independent* action than a bottle of drain cleaner, is labeled "cunning, baffling, and powerful." It is given a life of its own. Alcohol is considered to seduce and overpower human beings: "John Barleycorn calling me from the mantelpiece." When a grouper drinks himself to death, groupers take it as a warning, "The alcohol got him."

The newcomer may give up trying to understand the loaded language. He may attribute his difficulty in understanding to the "alcoholic fog" they imply he is in. Perhaps he will consider it wise to attend 90 meetings in 90 days. They say that is the smart thing to do. He can decide then.

This is the goal of the meeting with respect to the newcomer. He questions his own competence and wonders whether the AA members, apparently having recovered from that incompetence, have something to offer.

Chapter 10

On the "Broad Highway"

"[I]f you wish, you can join us on the Broad Highway"

— The Big Book

It is indeed a Broad Highway upon which the AA beginner sets out. The way is as wide as the eye can see. No restriction of any sort in sight. AA requires no beliefs, not even in God. One can pick one's own Higher Power. It can be God, the group, anything. One man even stayed sober with a doorknob for a Higher Power.

Members don't have to do anything. No one has to get a sponsor. No one has to work the steps. They are only suggestions. Membership is so easy that it is only necessary to *want* to stop drinking. You can even drink and be a member. For the new or prospective member, there is only the *suggestion* to make a commitment to 90 meetings in 90 days.

Information control is essential to cult indoctrination. The group must become the sole source of information about oneself. Communal cults like the Moonies, Hari-

Krishna and The Way* manage this through physical separation from other sources of information. The Moonies do this initially at three-day workshops held ostensibly for "world peace" or some other good cause. During the "workshops," members use the influence of a unanimous majority and hypnotic techniques to create confusion and distrust of the self in order to get a commitment from the prospective member to stay for an even longer indoctrination period.

In non-communal cults like AA, and the Oxford Group before them, physical isolation may be used. Oxford Group had their "hospital work" and AA has the alcohol and drug abuse treatment center where contact with friends and family is extremely limited. This degree of separation, however, is not entirely necessary. In AA, the commitment to 90 meetings in 90 days can greatly limit non-AA social contact. During this period of restricted social contact with "normies," every effort is made to discredit non-AA sources of information. The groupers become the sole source of credible information about oneself.

Imagine, for example, a man who works a 40 hour week. Daytime is spent at work. After work he heads for a meeting. The meeting lasts for one or two hours. He then is invited to coffee. He has the option of turning down the offer of Fellowship, and may want to since he hasn't seen his family all day. But, in thinking of his family, he may remember a speaker telling of how he almost lost his family for not taking advantage of the Fellowship or how the speaker lost his family altogether because he didn't put the program first. In any case, the

---

*The Way is a Christian cult. One of their requirements for female members is to prostitute themselves in order to draw potential recruits into the organization.

groupers are friendly and welcoming and he may have questions he wants to ask. Rather than spending time at home, the newcomer may be off for another hour or two, perhaps longer, for what can be considered informal indoctrination.

The groupers do not see themselves as having an ulterior motive. They sincerely want to help and will do their best to help in the same ways they were helped when they were new. They are fully prepared to "freely give that which was so freely given," partly because they know, at least in the back of their minds, that their lives depend on it.

AA newcomers are also encouraged to stay in phone contact with group members. To this end, the newcomer is encouraged to exchange phone numbers at meetings and to use them. With an obligation to call several groupers every day, calls to non-grouper friends and acquaintances decline.

The commitment to devote a great deal of time with groupers severely limits the time one spends with others and, more importantly, time alone with oneself to reflect on what is happening.

The newcomer who does manage to spend some time alone must deal with constant warnings about another symptom of alcoholism, the desire to "isolate." It is often considered one of the first symptoms of an incipient return to drinking. If someone misses a meeting he usually attends, he will be queried, out of genuine loving concern, as to where he was. If he doesn't have an acceptable reason, he will be cautioned about the dangers of "isolation."

For the newcomer, the "language of non-thought" is adopted, little by little. Words gain new meaning and the clichés begin having more and more meaning. As the new language is adopted, a linguistic barrier goes up between the new grouper and "normies." Normies gradually understand less and less. The newcomer and the groupers understand each other more and more.

Another way the new grouper is separated from others is with the advice to "stay out of slippery places." This does not mean just bars, but also parties, dinner parties and any kind of get-together where alcohol may be served. Since it is more the norm than the exception for alcohol to be served on social occasions, and this is especially true in the social circles of those who drink too much, the newcomer will probably feel it unwise to socialize with his friends. He will depend on the other groupers to fill this gap.

The most sinister form of separation practiced in AA is purely psychological and can be summed up with their cliché "Alcoholism is a family disease." The first and most important meaning of this cliché is that the alcoholic's spouse, children and parents are sick too; perhaps as sick as the alcoholic. The alcoholic is, and knows he is, to blame.[157] He is warned it is imperative, if he cares about his family, that he recover. To this end, he must put the Program first, even before his own family.* If he doesn't, he'll drink and lose them anyway. The family man who feels guilt over having put alcohol before his family is now encouraged to make up for it by putting AA before his family.

This, combined with adopting the loaded language, can drive a wedge between a man and his sick (insane, not under God-control) wife and children. Of course, AA has a solution. The family should be encouraged to work

---

*The roots of this are in one of the Big Book stories of "personal recovery" which is often paraphrased by groupers, "...I decided I must place this program above everything else, even my family, because if I did not maintain my sobriety I would lose my family anyway." p. 294

a spiritual program so they can recover too. Of course, this means working the Twelve Steps in Al-Anon.

Through various methods, among them hypnotic suggestion, sharing "personal experience" or "scientific fact," a new member may be led to believe that his family wants him to drink and hence, to die.* This is proved by family members refusing to be "in recovery," disagreeing with "spiritual principles," criticizing AA involvement or criticizing the new "alcoholic self." This generates suspicion and distrust between the alcoholic and the family which refuses to become groupers. *Where AA can't control sources of information, it discredits them.*

With time, AA becomes the sole source of credible information about oneself. Information from the world of "normies" isn't credible because they "don't understand." One's family and friends, if they drink, are in need of "a program." Even if they don't drink, family members are sick and in need. The only people who can give accurate information, the only sane, understanding people, are the alcoholic groupers because "They've lived it," "They have

---

*Sometimes the family actually does want the new AA member to drink. Often the most serious problem the family has had with the excessive drinker is that he has been emotionally and physically unavailable a great deal, if not most, of the time. When he joins AA, he may be even more unavailable. Whereas before he might have binged and been away mostly on weekends, now he is gone *every night*. What may be even worse, he quickly reaches a point where he has acquired AA's "spiritual way of life," meaning, in part, that he responds to the needs of his family with a cliché and a holier-than-thou attitude. The family may attribute all this to his not drinking, rather than to AA itself. They may decide they want the "old" person back and think they'll get him if he returns to drinking. This rarely, if ever, works. Once the drinker has adopted AA attitudes, his drinking is usually much worse. This only serves to prove to the drinker, and perhaps the family too, the wisdom of AA.

recovered," and "They have a spiritual program."

Information is also controlled between the elder groupers and the newcomer. During hours of informal indoctrination, such as at after-meeting coffee, the newcomer has the opportunity to ask questions of the elders.

If he asks the "right" questions, the newcomer gets direct, informative answers. Right questions are ones like, "How do I get a sponsor?" or "Where are there meetings on Wednesday nights?" The groupers will do their best to be as helpful and informative as possible.

Other questions call for the groupers to be helpful but not quite so informative. For instance, if a newcomer should ask about the religious tone of a meeting, he will be answered with the cliché, "AA is spiritual, not religious," and unlike religious organizations, "AA requires no beliefs." The newcomer is not told that everyone in the group holds certain beliefs in common. They hold the Big Book above both other religions and science, have special knowledge of God's Will and believe that those who don't "come to believe" face inevitable "jails, institutions, and death." He is not told that his religious beliefs are considered inferior and that, as he becomes more dependent on AA, great pressure will be brought to bear to change his belief system.*

Information control within the group is far from complete and the newcomer will occasionally see and hear things that contradict the sacred doctrine being held up to him as a way of stopping drinking and growing toward happiness, usefulness and wellness.

Perhaps someone with 20 years will tell of having just beat his wife "for the last time." This, of course, will be told in the context of spiritual growth achieved through

---

*The superimposition of AA beliefs over religious beliefs is covered in the chapter on the steps.

working the Program. If the newcomer questions the effectiveness of the Program or the speaker's "recovery," there are many ways he may be helped to understand. These situations come up so frequently there are many clichés to deal with them. Among them are, "He has Time. What can you say about yourself?" and "Alcoholics are too judgmental. You must consider where he started from," and perhaps most popular, "Point a finger at someone else, and you are pointing three at yourself." These clichés and others point out the deficiencies and status of the newcomer. He must be helped to understand. He doesn't have Time so he can't understand. It is absolutely untrue that the Program has flaws. It was spiritually inspired. It is also unspiritual to be critical of others, especially of the Elders. He may be told "you must never be critical of others, but always hard on yourself." The elder groupers may reply by telling how they themselves used to be judgmental and how it nearly caused them to drink and die.

If the newcomer doesn't accept the wise, helpful words offered, he may be told in a loving way that he is too new or not yet spiritual enough to understand. He may be told, "As the Big Book says, more will be revealed if you work the program." However, if the newcomer is persistent in seeking explanations of inconsistencies, the groupers may point out the newcomer's obvious insanity with, "Well then, why don't you just go drink!" This is very strong language and is only used with the most obstinate cases. However, it does point out the truth of the Program: to think one sees flaws in it is evidence of alcoholism's cunning, baffling, and powerful influence over the mind. Attempts at critical analysis of the Program, or criticism of the Elders, is merely alcohol's evil influence. The newcomer obviously wants to drink.

One of the most potent forces of mind control is the

subtle coercion of public statements. The first statement elicited publicly from the newcomer is, "I am an alcoholic." Depending on the structure of the meeting attended, it may be said at the very first meeting with little or no thought given to the implications. In some meetings, everyone in the room takes turns introducing themselves by their first name and "disease." Perhaps 25 or 50 people will identify themselves uniformly with their first name and "I am an alcoholic." Then it is up to the pigeon. If he doesn't want to stand out, there is only one choice: to say "I am an alcoholic." He may have his own idea of what an alcoholic is and feel comfortable stating he is "an alcoholic." In mind control cults there is rarely if ever any physical coercion. Situations are staged so that people choose "on their own" either the desired course or from only desired options. The pigeon has the option of merely stating his first name. At this point, even this may be desirable for indoctrination purposes. He may then wonder what he is doing there and whether he is suffering "denial."

Often, out of deference to the room full of friendly faces gazing at him, he will splutter in embarrassment, "I guess I am an alcoholic." All groupers smile knowingly and affectionately. They understand that this is a milestone in his "recovery." The pigeon has no idea.

This public admission of being an alcoholic, whether the newcomer knows it yet or not, is the beginning of the acceptance of the authority of AA. Since he is an alcoholic, and has publicly acknowledged himself as such, he must defer to the unanimous opinion of the experts on alcoholism gathered about him for defining who he is. In AA, by definition, an alcoholic is someone who must work the Steps and follow other "suggestions" or die.

"Unless each A.A. member follows to the best of his ability our suggested Twelve Steps of recovery, he almost certainly signs his own death warrant. ... We *must* obey certain principles, or we die." [158]

A newcomer would reject out of hand being told that if he didn't work the Steps he would probably die. To get by this, groupers continuously acknowledge the Steps as "suggestive only." They then proceed to tell how they nearly died or how others died because their diseased minds told them they didn't need to work the steps. Another way the newcomer becomes afraid to not work the steps is through sincere, genuine fear expressed by the elders through body language. For example, if a newcomer says in casual conversation that he doesn't need the Steps, he's staying sober just fine without them, the groupers will fall silent. Bodies stiffen. All eyes, filled with fear, apprehension or disapproval, will focus on the newcomer. Without verbally contradicting the newcomer, the message is given. Once the message has been non-verbally transmitted, the ice may be broken by an elder reminding everyone, "Like the Big Book says, the Steps are but suggestive only." This is a reminder to the groupers of the Big Book injunction against "preaching" and other forms of open coercion. It is also ostensibly support for the newcomer's position. Everyone knows the Steps are suggestive only. No one has to do anything they don't want to in AA. While the newcomer gets verbal "defense" for not working the Steps, he is also reminded it is a suggestion. He knows that, as a suggestion, it is the opinion of the unanimous majority that if he continues to be obstinate in not following it, he is "signing his own death warrant."

In adapting to his new "social circle," the newcomer learns which comments bring approval and which bring disapproval. People are so kind, friendly and understanding, it is, at the very least, impolite to upset them. The only way to avoid this is to agree. One quickly learns to at least express, if not quite believe, only acceptable ideas.

In the interest of "recovery" the newcomer is also encouraged to share at meetings.* First-time sharers usually have little to say but they have had others model sharing for them. The nervous newcomer can feel safe announcing how much Time he has. Announcing "I have three days" will be interrupted with a round of applause and perhaps shouts of approval. He is rewarded for telling how he has found the truth of a cliché or other piece of doctrine. Sharing how the Program is working for him always brings warm applause and caring attention. Also much approved by the congregation is any statement of confession or any statement derogatory towards himself: He is "getting honest" and showing "humility."

However, any statement contradictory to AA doctrine, even if it doesn't bring immediate boos or derisive laughter, will bring explanation, warnings and "understanding" from the elder groupers who share later. The "understanding" usually takes the form of, "He is still new and hasn't learned yet." The warnings are usually given indirectly, the elders all "coincidentally" focusing their sharing on other people they know who hold the same opinions. These "other people" either have died or are drinking and will die soon if they don't see the light.

Sooner or later the newcomer comes to see the importance of working the Steps. To this end, he must find a sponsor because, "This is a 'we' Program," and "It is

---

*I have heard (but not seen) that in some areas of the country, newcomers are not encouraged to share, but to "sit down, shut up, and learn something."

dangerous to take the spiritual path alone."

The newcomer must ask an elder to be his sponsor. Among the suggestions on how to pick a good sponsor are to find someone who "has what you want," meaning someone you hold as ideal. Also important is selecting someone who has a similar social status, drinking history and interests and at least a year or two of Time. The newcomer is often cautioned against picking someone with too much Time because they are sure to be too spiritually advanced and recovered for the newcomer to relate to.

The newcomer, believing doing so will keep him sober and allow him to share in the recovery he sees in the meetings, is now ready to work The Twelve Steps of Alcoholics Anonymous...

Chapter 11

The Road of Happy Destiny

"We shall be with you in the Fellowship of the Spirit as you trudge the Road of Happy Destiny."
– The Big Book

The Twelve Steps are the core of the Alcoholics Anonymous "spiritual program." They are held as "spiritually inspired" so they are beyond question. It is normal, however, for the newcomer to ask how or why they work. The answer is, being "spiritually inspired," they are above human logic and understanding but it is logical to work them because they have been "proven" to really work. The newcomer is surrounded by the proof; the other cult members.

Sooner or later the newcomer feels a need to work the Steps. He comes to understand, since it is so often pointed out, how much benefit comes from working them. Whenever he approaches an elder with a problem, he is likely to be reminded that he hasn't worked the Steps with the implication that this is the root of his problem.

The presumed benefits of working a spiritual program are formalized as "The Promises." Taken from the Big Book, they often take a central position in meetings either as a sacred reading or as a topic of general discussion, "How have the Promises been fulfilled in your life?"

"If we are painstaking about this phase of our development, we will be amazed before we are half way through. We are going to know a new freedom and a new happiness. We will not regret the past nor wish to shut the door on it. We will comprehend the word serenity and we will know peace. No matter how far down the scale we have gone, we will see how our experience can benefit others. That feeling of uselessness and self-pity will disappear. We will lose interest in selfish things and gain interest in our fellows. Self-seeking will slip away. Our whole attitude and outlook upon life will change. Fear of people and of economic insecurity will leave us. We will intuitively know how to handle situations which used to baffle us. We will suddenly realize that God is doing for us what we could not do for ourselves.

Are these extravagant promises? ...They will always materialize if we work for them."[159]

Against these Promises is the certainty of "jails, institutions, and death." The newcomer wants to work the Steps.

Co-founder Bill Wilson, author of the Big Book and the most celebrated recovery in AA, after ten or fifteen years of working the Steps, undertook to write the definitive manual on how to work them. In this manual, called "The Twelve Steps and Twelve Traditions," Wilson describes the value of the Steps,

"A.A.'s Twelve Steps are a group of principles, spiritual in their nature, which, if practiced as a way of life, can expel the obsession to drink and enable the sufferer to become happily and usefully whole."[160]

151

Eight years after he was "changed" by Ebby from the Oxford Group and five years after he originally penned the Twelve Steps, Bill Wilson was somewhat less than "happily and usefully whole."
From AA's own literature,

> "[H]e was plunged into an abyss of such bleakness and negativity as to make him suicidal."[161]

This depression lasted for eleven years during which time he wrote the book to help others become "happily and usefully whole."

AA member Marty Mann, who was busy "educating America about alcoholism" with her National Council on Alcoholism, described Wilson during this period,

> "It was awful. There were long periods of time when he couldn't get out of bed. He just stayed in bed, and Lois would see that he ate."[162]

From his personal secretary,

> "He would come down to the office many times and sit across from me and just put his head in his hands and really not be able to communicate...,"[163]

and an AA general manager,

> "There were some times when these horrible depressions would go on and on, for days and days."[164]

Apparently, no official account of Wilson's depression was given until the 1984 publication of "Pass It On." No one seemed to have found it ironic that a man suffering *severe chronic depression* was claiming to have the secret to becoming "usefully and happily whole."

An indoctrinated cult member, Bill Wilson was

incapable of questioning the doctrine even though his personal experience was the opposite of that promised. An examination of the Twelve Steps shows why the thoroughly indoctrinated member is incapable of questioning the doctrine even when belief causes great harm.

There is much within the Twelve Steps which leads to severe emotional problems including suicidal depression. Depression is characterized by feelings of powerlessness and helplessness. It is also based in the suppression of one's emotions, most particularly anger. Rather than being a prescription for becoming "happily and usefully whole," the Twelve Steps are a prescription for helplessness, self-alienation and depression. They result in the problem drinker becoming *more addicted to furthering cult goals than he ever was to alcohol.*

Step One: "We admitted we were powerless over alcohol — that our lives had become unmanageable."

This Step, for the AA sponsor or treatment center therapist, is what Bill Wilson referred to as "tilling the black soil of hopelessness."[165] It is made up of two distinct parts; an admission of "powerlessness" and an admission of "unmanageability." The unmanageable part is where the "baby," "pigeon" or "patient" is to list, often in writing, how unmanageable his life is as evidence of his alcoholism. This includes anything a person has done contradictory to his own values or society's rules. It usually goes no further back than the "first drink." The "baby" must figure out how *everything* that is not right with his life, its "unmanageability," is directly tied to alcohol and alcoholism.

The pigeon has the problem of resolving guilt over his past actions. He can either admit that alcohol is responsible for everything and gain status and warm regard or insist that he is responsible and "be in denial" and lose status and regard.

Part of the admission of alcoholism may be preparing a list of one's history of alcohol and drug consumption including quantity and frequency. The goal of this exercise is to convince the newcomer to accept that he is under the influence of a disease, not his own influence. At the same time he is pressured to give a "public" admission, "I am powerless." This admission can take various forms. In a treatment center it may be "getting honest" in a "group therapy" session. Outside of the treatment centers, it may be as simple as getting on one's knees and admitting one's powerlessness and unmanageability to God and the groupers present.

Exactly how this is done is unimportant. The important point is that confession is made. The core of this admission is that alcoholism is a disease with a life of its own. Devil Drink, "the rapacious creditor, bleeds us of all self-sufficiency and all will to resist." The "alcoholic" is totally at the mercy of Devil Drink. The admission of powerlessness is an admission that one is faced with death and nothing within oneself, nor any "human power," can help.

The Twelve Steps and Twelve Traditions (12 & 12) suggests that those who doubt their powerlessness should be told to go ahead and drink. This is, of course, without encouraging them to get help for underlying problems or even acknowledging that they may exist. The intent is to "plant the seed" that the target for indoctrination will indeed be powerless (learn helplessness), as happened with Bill Wilson after being "treated" by Dr. Silkworth. The 12 & 12 suggests this is a highly effective method.

"It was then discovered that when one alcoholic had planted in the mind of another the true nature of his malady, that person could never be the same again.

Following every spree, he would say to himself, 'Maybe those A.A.'s were right...'"[166]

In a treatment center, it is not possible to suggest someone drink. However, there are other ways to convince the indoctrinees that they are incapable of moderating or quitting without AA. One of these is the "scientific" lecture. Medical "authorities" give lectures on "the disease." Using unnamed scientific studies, the lecturer presents, in the presumed context of a non-AA lecture, "the medical facts," just as was done by Dr. Silkworth. These lectures include the "scientific certainties" of genetic defects, brain differences, loss of control, denial and inevitable progression.

Those who come to believe AA's "One drink, one drunk," can't moderate their drinking. Once a newcomer learns he is "powerless over alcohol," he is suffering from a form of learned helplessness. He "knows," just like the inner-city school children who "couldn't" learn to read, that any effort is "wasted." He automatically, subconsciously, can't even try.

No one can reasonably argue that someone who drinks self-destructively shouldn't be helped to see the damage he does to himself so he'll stop. This is not quite what AA does. They convince a prospect for membership that *a force outside his control is killing him and that without AA he'll die.*

"Under the lash of alcoholism, we are driven to A.A., and there we discover the fatal nature of our situation. Then and only then, do we become as open-minded to conviction and as willing to listen as the dying can be."[167]

At the end of working Step One, the new grouper has made a "public statement" of "powerlessness" and "unmanageablity." He has confessed that he has no resources to stop the "inevitable progression" of alcoholism.

If the first Step has been worked properly, Devil Drink, alias alcoholism, begins taking its place as the primary driving force in the life of the new cult member. Before, the newcomer may have wondered why he drank the way he did. Now he "knows" he has a disease. While fear of death from drinking is now the primary motivating factor in the newcomer's life, he may feel *relieved* at this point. He is no longer responsible, at least for the moment, for *anything* he has done in his past. It is not his fault, he has a disease. Devil Drink made him do it.

If the sponsor and other groupers have properly "till[ed] the black soil of hopelessness," the new grouper is now "open-minded" and ready for Step Two.

Step Two: Came to believe that a Power greater than ourselves could restore us to sanity.

Step Two, to the uninitiated, appears to be mostly about finding faith in God. While there may be some truth in this, working this Step is more a matter of defining God in AA's image. However, that is actually only half of the Step and, without first working the other half, one is not *ready* to "come to believe" the AA doctrine to be presented.

"Restoration to sanity" implies that the newcomer is insane. While his insanity may be clear to the elder groupers who have worked the Steps, the "baby" must be helped to understand the full depths of his insanity. This takes help from his sponsor and other groupers or the treatment center "therapist" because "Some will be willing to term themselves 'problem drinkers,' but cannot endure the suggestion that they are in fact mentally ill."[168] In other words, even if someone admits that he drinks too much, decides to stop and go for treatment, he still needs to understand that he is "mentally ill." By AA definition, an alcoholic is insane, "[N]o alcoholic... can claim 'soundness of mind' for himself."[169] From the Big Book, "the main problem of the alcoholic centers in his mind, rather than in his body."[170] Of course, it is reasonable to argue that drinking to self-destructive excess and the outrageous behavior that may accompany it is insane behavior. This Step, however, goes much further.

The "baby" or patient may be assigned to write out, in detail, all the evidence of his insanity. This generally begins with the obvious; prior drinking behavior. It also extends to "insane" emotions and "alcoholic thinking." The goal is to get the pigeon to accept that he is insane, must distrust himself entirely and is doomed to death without "a spiritual program." He is to rely on the AA elders who, due to the Program, are "miracles of mental health."

Little did the pigeon imagine when he first acknowledged "I am an alcoholic" that he was acknowledging his insanity. He may have had his own definition of an alcoholic but he now learns that to be an alcoholic is to be insane. All of the other groupers admit to their insanity. Those with more Time, of course, are much less insane than the newcomer. Their acknowledgement of their own insanity when they were new makes it easier for the pigeon to see and accept his insanity.

By accepting his "insanity," the pigeon, already under the threat of death, becomes totally dependent on the elder groupers. Any difference in thought and opinion from the elders or the sacred text is now merely a sign of his insanity. The elders often, usually "lovingly" but sometimes not so lovingly, remind him he is insane. *He can no longer trust his own thoughts and perceptions; he has the disease, he is sick, he is an alcoholic, he is insane.*

Believing he is insane and will die without AA, the newcomer is confronted with the "fact" that he is "doomed to an alcoholic death or to live on a spiritual basis."[171] He is now ready to begin putting faith in a "Power greater than" himself. This Power is most often referred to in AA as "Higher Power" or "HP."

The job now for the AA sponsor or treatment center therapist is to secure the position of AA either as God or the only viable source of interpretation of God's Will.

AA literature and members frequently boast of the Program as being "spiritual, not religious." This is partly because they discarded the Bible. The core of their argument, however, is that no beliefs are required for membership. This is true, sort of. However, in order to bother with attending, one must believe AA has something to offer. It is also necessary to confess to having the disease to attend many meetings or to fully participate in other than a newcomer's meeting. To fit in with AA's social system, to gain status and avoid being patronized, shunned, ridiculed or taking the "sicker than others seat," one must begin accepting the doctrine. The core of the teachings is that one must work the Steps in order to survive the machinations of Devil Drink. In order to work Step Two, one must choose a Higher Power.

For someone who believes in God, this would seem to be a rather perfunctory "God is my HP." For the atheist or agnostic, it appears to present a difficult problem but AA has the simplest of solutions. You don't need to believe in God. You can make AA your "higher power."

> "You can, if you wish, make A.A. itself your 'higher power.' Here's a very large group of people who have solved their alcohol problem. In this respect they are certainly a power greater than you, who have not even come close to a solution. Surely you can have faith in them."[172]

For the believer in God who has his own religion or

denomination, things are a bit touchier. AA must elevate itself above the recruit's religion without leaving itself open to accusations of doing so. The 12 & 12 attacks the pigeon himself on the basis of "quality of faith." In typical AA "humble" fashion, the words "we," "us" and "alcoholics" are used in all accusations.

> "...has to do with the quality of faith rather than its quantity. This has been our blind spot. We supposed we had humility when really we hadn't. ...The fact was we really hadn't cleaned house so that the grace of God could enter us and expel the obsession. In no deep or meaningful sense had we ever taken stock of ourselves, made amends to those we had harmed, or freely given to any other human being without any demand for reward. We had not even prayed rightly."[173]

These and other discounts of the newcomer's religious practice are immediately followed by attacks on the person's soundness of mind in the customary indirect "we," "us" and "alcoholics" fashion.

> "Few indeed are the practicing alcoholics who have any idea how irrational they are, or seeing their irrationality can bear to face it. ... [N]o alcoholic ... can claim 'soundness of mind' for himself."[174]

This is the way the pigeon will be dealt with from this point forward. Before he has a chance to think things through and present, even to himself, a reasonable argument against what he is told, he will be reminded that, as one of "us," an alcoholic, he is irrational, mentally ill, evilly motivated, suffering from "alcoholic thinking" and insane.

From the Second Step onward, he will be told how to relate to his "Higher Power." His religion may offer eternal reward, but if he doesn't follow "direction," AA's word for Oxford Group's Guidance, Devil Drink will send him to that reward sooner than he cares to go.

In order to understand the Program and its relationship to religion, it is helpful to go back to AA's roots in the Oxford Group. Oxford Group's goal was to convert the entire world to God-control and establish the ideal government, a "God-control led Fascist dictatorship."[175] Members were to attend churches, but not to worship God or as a path toward closeness with Him. They didn't need it. They had Guidance, a direct link to God, and they had their own meetings. Their purpose was the "humble" goal of *reforming the churches*. They didn't attend the various denominations out of a belief in their creed. They were there to help the lost sheep, to guide them to the Oxford Group.

AA's relation to other religions is descended from this. Early AA recommended church attendance. Quite often, individual AA members and groups still do. Bill Wilson's views, published in "Pass It On," were more or less that, in spite of all the terrible things religions have done, religions are good in that there is a great deal of spirituality in religion. Of course, AA is the only "purely spiritual" organization. AA was very careful in their early literature to say nothing which would be overtly contradictory to any particular Christian denomination. They even made a point of defending organized religion (but only in the context of an attack on atheists and agnostics). They never attack religion, only the practitioner. In the lengthy quote above, the newcomer is attacked for his "quality of faith." When the pigeon accepts that he does indeed have shortcomings in this area, he isn't told to return to his church to "set himself right with God." He is told to continue with the Steps in order to "fit himself into God's plan."

The "observations" about alcoholics, better stated as attacks against the pigeon, ostensibly deal with themes consistent with almost all religions. They are, however, actually peculiar in that they are charges, in AA's own language and terms, that the newcomer hasn't worked all the Steps. For instance, "we supposed we had humility when we really hadn't" points out the need to work Step Seven which specifically addresses "humility" in an AA context. The accusation of never having "really cleaned house" is a call to work Step Four and Step Five, taking a "fearless moral inventory" and "admitting defects of character." "Never made amends" means one needs to work Step Eight and Step Nine. Regardless of how the pigeon takes it, the accusation of never having "freely given to another human being" has absolutely nothing to do with Christian, or any other kind, of charity. It has to do with working Step Twelve, which is "carrying the message." The message, of course, has nothing to do with any religious or spiritual convictions the pigeon may have separate from AA. It is Oxford Group's call to practice the Five C's; to convert others to Oxford Group. It is nothing more or less than a call to carry AA's message, to indoctrinate others into AA.

The accusation of not having prayed properly is perhaps the most insidious of all. By discounting and, most importantly, getting the pigeon to discount, his private communication with God, AA becomes the intermediary, interpreter and authority in just what God has to say.

The nature and depth of this change to "God-control" becomes clearer with an understanding of the ensuing Steps.

Step Three: Made a decision to turn our will and our lives over to the care of God <u>as we understood God.</u>

Whatever "Higher Power" one has selected, in this

Step, the indoctrinee is to begin acting and thinking on the basis of the desire of this Higher Power and begin depending on it for all things rather than his own *insane* thoughts and desires. Any objection to any part of this Step will bring a loving reminder of the Step Two admission of insanity and Step One admission of unmanageability.

According to the 12 & 12's discussion of this Step, affirmative action is necessary to "cut away the self-will which has always blocked the entry of God ... or Higher Power."[176] The reason one's "Higher Power" need not be "God" becomes clear,

> "Isn't it true that in all matters touching upon alcohol, each of them has decided to turn his or her life over to the care, protection, and guidance of Alcoholics Anonymous? ... Now if this is not turning one's will and life over to a newfound Providence, then what is it?"[177]

There is no distinction made between Alcoholics Anonymous and God in AA theology. Since their literature, particularly the Big Book, and the Twelve Steps are "spiritually inspired," and the existence of the organization itself is a direct act of God, *turning one's "will and life" over to Alcoholics Anonymous is the same as turning it over to God.*

After stating that turning one's will and life over to the care of AA is turning it over to Providence, the new grouper is customarily attacked. To argue against turning everything over to "Something or Somebody else" is,

> "[T]he process by which instinct and logic always seek to bolster egotism, and so frustrate spiritual development."[178]

The trouble with "this kind of thinking," thinking perhaps that God *gave us* our will and our lives as a precious gift, is, according to the 12 & 12, that it "takes no real account of the facts."[179] The Orwellian "facts" are,

> "The more we become willing to depend upon a Higher Power, the more independent we actually are. Therefore dependence, as A.A. practices it, is really a means of gaining true independence of the spirit."[180]

AA, like all mind-control cults, seeks to control the inner world of intellectual experience. This control isn't limited to loaded language. One is taught that he doesn't have a right to think his own thoughts. His thinking should be "on a higher plane."

> "How persistently we claim the right to decide all by ourselves just what we shall think..."[181]

Not only does the AA member not have a right to his own thoughts, this restriction extends to emotional life as will be detailed in Step Four. AA members are taught to disrupt their own thinking with thought-stopping techniques. The most popular way in AA is *ostensibly* through prayer, "Thy will, not mine, be done."* This phrase or an entire prayer is to be said "In all times of emotional disturbance..."[182]

Among the times a newcomer is likely to suffer "emotional disturbance" is any time a thought overtly contradictory to AA doctrine comes to mind. This is when the thought stopping technique has its most powerful and negative effect. In AA, it is sincerely

---

*A member of Co-dependents Anonymous, an organization which like AA considers the Twelve Steps the inspired word of God, recommended to me another thought-stopping technique, to say to oneself, "Cancel, cancel, blue sky" and then imagine the sky. It serves the same purpose, is considered spiritual, and has the same effect as the one line "prayer." It interferes with thinking.

believed that AA comes from God, and that critical thoughts about AA are evilly ("disease") motivated. The "disease" is to be suppressed in oneself, and this means suppressing "alcoholic thinking." The AA member quickly learns to "stop" all negative thoughts about AA. While there is some permission to think thoughts critical of certain members, particularly those with less Time, and even to think critically of some meetings, without the capacity to think negative thoughts about the AA doctrine itself, it comes to be rationalized and seen as perfect. One doesn't see a flaw in the doctrine and adapt the doctrine. One *thinks* (alcoholicly, of course) one sees a flaw in the doctrine, and works to "understand" where the flaw is in oneself.

This is closely tied to "honesty" in AA. The doctrine, being "spiritually inspired" is perfect. If one's life experience doesn't fit the doctrine, it isn't the doctrine that is wrong, the person isn't *really* honest. A great deal of "progress" in "getting honest" and "spiritual growth" has occurred in the first three Steps. In Step One, the pigeon has "gotten honest" in admitting the Power of alcohol and his own Powerlessness in the face of it. In Step Two, the pigeon has "gotten honest" in acknowledging that AA is a Power capable of defeating Devil Drink and acknowledging that he is insane and cannot trust his own thoughts. In Step Three, he must "get honest" on the need to turn his "will and life" over to AA/God. Out of "honesty" he begins to work for the "willingness" to discard the self which he learned in Step Two is insane. He is to work to make his own thoughts go away.

The consummation of this Step may be the recitation of the "Third Step Prayer." In this prayer, the grouper prays, "Relieve me of the bondage of self, that I may better do Thy will."[183]

The following two Steps, four and five, can be considered together.

Step Four: Made a searching and fearless moral inventory of ourselves.

Step Five: Admitted to God, to ourselves, and to another human being the exact nature of our wrongs

Great expectations are built up for working these Steps in AA literature and in the meetings. Groupers bear witness to their life-changing effects. They speak of new-found Serenity or a new awareness of their Higher Power. The Big Book promises "we are delighted. ...We can be alone at perfect ease and peace. Our fears fall from us."[184] The 12 & 12 promises "a healing tranquility"[185] and holds out the promise of becoming "conscious of God as they never were before"[186] upon the completion of Step Five.

Step Four, the "moral inventory," is much more than a written confession of sins or "defects of character." In preparation for writing out the inventory, evil is redefined according to the AA "world view." In the writing, one redefines oneself, and one's past, in the AA image. The stress is on evil or sin, usually referred to as "defects of character." It is a complete switch from the "outsider doctrine"* of alcoholism being a medical disease to being

---

*All cults have different levels of truth. "Outsider doctrine" refers to information and "truths" which are told to the general public. Complementary to this "outsider doctrine" is "insider doctrine" which is revealed to members alone and then usually only gradually as they attain status. For example, the outsider doctrine of the Scientologists is that their organization works for mental health and human potential. The insider doctrine includes belief in past lives on other planets and other unusual beliefs. The reason for this separation of

a "spiritual malady." In Step One, the alcoholic's problem is "external" in the sense of "not attributable to self." The alcoholic has a "disease." His problems are due to the power of alcohol/Devil Drink. However, by the Fourth Step, the stress is now on alcoholism as a "spiritual disease." Although rarely bluntly stated, it is believed to be caused by moral failings. Whereas in Step One the blame is on "the disease," by Step Four, the "baby" knows, "...our troubles are basically of our own making."[187]

The Big Book discussion of the Fourth Step begins, "being convinced that self, manifested in various ways, was what had defeated us..."[188]

Principle among the "manifestations of self" is normal human emotion.

Anger, usually referred to as resentment, is considered the "number one offender."

> "But with the alcoholic, whose hope is the maintenance and growth of a spiritual experience, this business of resentment is infinitely grave. We found that it is fatal. For when harboring such feelings we shut ourselves off from the sunlight of the Spirit. The insanity of alcohol returns and we drink again. And with us, to drink is to die.

---

doctrine in cults is that it would be impossible to recruit if people knew what the organization really was about. The line is not always sharp and clear between the two "levels of truth." I have heard AA members on radio interviews speak in detail of alcoholism as a spiritual disease. Normally, all that "should" be said is that it is a fatal, progressive and incurable disease. Saying "spiritual disease" is too much of a tip-off to the true nature of "the Program." It might turn away "those who could have been helped."

If we were to live, we had to be free of anger."[189*]

One of the recommended ways to not be angry is to use thought stopping techniques. When one becomes aware of anger, one is to say to oneself, "God save me from being angry. Thy will be done."[190]

AA members have two motivations for not allowing themselves to experience anger. One is that it is "unspiritual;" it is a sin.[191] The other, demonstrated in the above quotation from the Big Book, is that the grouper fears he will die if he allows himself to experience his anger. While fear is the primary motivation for the grouper to suppress awareness of his anger, he is unlikely, with the accumulation of Time, to *feel* afraid or even be aware that it is such a major motivator of his behavior.

In Step Four, he also learns he must suppress awareness of the "evil and corroding thread" of fear. Although, beginning with Step One, his primary motivation in life is fear, the grouper doesn't maintain awareness of it. Being aware of what is going on within himself would be "dangerous," "evil," "unspiritual" and "useless." The areas of emotional life which are to be disowned, for one to become unaware of, also includes a broad range of emotions termed "self-pity" including sadness, loneliness and feelings of hopelessness or helplessness.

Self-confidence is also considered a liability.

"Some of us once had great self-confidence, but it didn't fully solve the fear problem, or any other. When it made us cocky, it was worse."[192]

---

*While the 12 & 12 makes it clear that sin and defects of character are one and the same, in conversation, groupers never use the word sin. It just sounds too religious. The "spiritual" phrase, defects of character, is used.

There are many direct correlations between AA's scorn for normal human emotion and thought and the attitudes expressed in the addictive family system. In the addictive family system, the child's awareness and perceptions are discounted. In AA, the member's awareness is called "alcoholic thinking." The child is taught that the experience of various emotions is wrong. AA teaches the same. The child in the addictive family system is caught in the bind of figuring out how he is wrong. In AA, the grouper is in the same bind. The doctrine and the elders are never wrong; something is wrong with the grouper. AA extends this "wrongness" and "badness" of the alcoholic. *Any time the alcoholic is upset about anything it is a sure sign that something is wrong with him.*

> "Though a situation had not been entirely our fault, we tried to disregard the other person involved entirely. Where were we to blame?"[193]

With the various "manifestations of self" fully defined, the grouper is ready to write out a thorough confession of his sins from the perspective of "alcoholic" or "bad child." Much more than a confession of sin, it is also a redefinition of the self and the adoption of a "repentant sinner" role. In writing one's "moral inventory," all important events in one's life are looked at and written from the "I am a sinner" perspective.

Many versions of Step Four exist from the original Big Book version to its expansion in the 12 & 12 to various "recovery house" versions to those unique to individual AA sponsors. They are all to be written and all are unanimous in that the "manifestations of self," whatever they are called, are to be identified. Each version opens

---

*See "Acceptance," in the Big Book on p. 449 and the 12 & 12, p. 90.

doors to the possibility of guilt in various areas the author thinks likely to be overlooked by the indoctrinee.

This is an extremely emotional period for the new grouper. Not only is he bringing up painful incidents going all the way back to childhood that "proved" him "bad," but he is to accept in his adult consciousness that he is, indeed, "bad." Every incident which provoked fear, anger, sadness, hurt or loneliness is looked at from the perspective that, in some way or another, he alone was wrong. He is a sinner. He is guilty. It is easy, in terms of AA doctrine, for him to see how defective he is. Even if he displayed little or no "bad behavior," he certainly had emotional responses. If one of the major events in his life was the death of his parents, he certainly sinned and sinned greatly. Since the normal response of children who lose parents is to feel sad, lonely, hurt, helpless, angry and afraid, it is obvious to the grouper that he was guilty of self-pity, resentment, fear and "alcoholic sensitivity." The grouper is to understand that allowing these emotions to exist is the "real" problem. This points to one of the main purposes of Step Four, the institution of emotional control. The indoctrinee is to work to understand that allowing the existence of "self" was the cause of all ill effects. For example, the member who lost his parents as a child *rationalizes*, from the AA perspective, and *comes to believe* that his childhood experience of "self-pity, resentment, fear and alcoholic sensitivity" was the *cause of problems*. In carefully defining prior emotional experience as bad, any current emotional awareness is also seen as bad. The grouper *has new reasons* to work to suppress it.

As the indoctrinee works on Step Four, he very likely can't help letting off a lot of steam from pent up emotions. As he writes of past traumatic experiences, he may share some of the pain with his sponsor, with fellow groupers or at meetings. This is accepted, even encouraged, during the "honeymoon" period.* Later displays of emotion will be seen as a sign of not "working the Program" since the Program is supposed to make "bad" feelings go away.

As the time for the Step Five confession approaches, he is likely to find he has certain secrets that he would prefer to "take to the grave." However, he knows that it is essential that he reveal these in order to avoid a return to the bottle and death. Fear of exposure adds to his emotional turmoil. He may consider only telling God. However, the 12 & 12 is very clear on the necessity of making confession with "another human being." One of the "reasons" is that "being alone with God doesn't seem as embarrassing as facing up to another person."[194] Another is that being honest with God alone is "largely theoretical."[195]

While the Big Book is very careful to suggest that "Those of us belonging to a religious denomination which requires confession must, and of course, will want to go to the properly appointed authority...,"[196] the later 12 & 12 stresses the need for "someone who is experienced, who not only has stayed dry but has been able to surmount other serious difficulties. Difficulties, perhaps, like our own."[197]

Another difference between the discussion of Step Five in the older (1939) Big Book and the newer (1952) 12 & 12 is the reintroduction of the word "guidance" from the Oxford Group, but now without the capital "G." The word is missing altogether from the Big Book version of this

---

*Most cults have a "honeymoon" period for the new member, during which time he is "tolerated" and catered to. In most cults, as in AA, it lasts about six months.

Step, which was written at a time when AA was attempting to hide its association.

The resurrected word "guidance" explains the need to confess to another.

> "[P]eople of very high spiritual development almost always insist on checking ... the guidance they feel they have received from God. Surely, then, a novice ought not lay himself open to the chance of making foolish, perhaps tragic, blunders in this fashion."[198]

While admitting that checking guidance* may not be infallible, the literature makes clear that it is better than one's own prayer and meditation.

> "[I]t is likely to be far more specific than any direct guidance we may receive while we are still so inexperienced in establishing contact with a Power greater than ourselves."[199]

Notice that those who "check guidance" are those who have more experience in "establishing contact with a Power greater." It is another way of saying those with Time.

While working Step Four, there is usually a tremendous amount of emotional release, although the subjective experience may be that the more some feelings are expressed, the more other feelings mysteriously appear. "A Conviction of the hideousness of his own personal guilt," combined with increasing fear as the time for confession approaches, creates an emotional peaking of both guilt and fear. Combined with this great guilt and

---

*An AA member would never say "check guidance," and would in all likelihood be only dimly, if at all, aware of the Oxford Group expression. He would call it "get direction."

fear is an expectancy of "Serenity" just around the corner.

If the confession has been thoroughly prepared and "nothing is held back," the grouper may well have his expectations fulfilled. If so, AA has proved the Power of the Steps in bringing about Serenity. However, if he doesn't have some sort of peak experience, it is his own fault. Perhaps he wasn't honest and thorough even if he thinks he was. Any time the grouper claims the Promises aren't being fulfilled in his life, he is opening himself up to group censure and risking loss of status. If the Program isn't working, as the popular cliché "Some are sicker than others" suggests, the grouper is one of the sicker ones.

If he genuinely believes he was "honest and thorough," for him to insist that he was but isn't receiving the "payoff," would be a symptom that he is one of the "unfortunates." As the opening of Chapter Five of the Big Book suggests, he may be "incapable of being honest" with himself. "Unfortunates" seem to "have been born that way." The wise grouper soon learns the wisdom of pretending. One of the more popular clichés is "Stick with the winners." If he doesn't "act as if" (pretend) he is "happily and usefully whole" and the "honeymoon period" is over, the other groupers may decide he isn't a winner and, to protect their own precious "Serenity," may decline to associate with him. At the very least, they will show scorn and contempt or be extremely patronizing.

Even if the grouper has a peak experience, which most do, it is unlikely to last for more than a few hours or days. He has let off a great deal of emotional pressure, taken away the fear of confession and alleviated guilt. But he now has his *self* defined as "defective" or "sinful" to a degree that is rarely learned even in the addictive family system. Where, in childhood, the alcoholic learns parts of his self are "bad" in a "haphazard" or "random" manner, in AA the definition of the self as bad and useless is extremely thorough.

A partial list of "bad" parts of the self, those which are "defects of character," includes anger, sadness, loneliness, fear, being "too happy," feeling self-confident and being sensitive. Other manifestations of self include self-knowledge, having hopes and dreams (ambitions), one's own thoughts, one's own will and the instincts.

Not only is most of the self defined as bad, but in a very bizarre, limited way, tiny parts of the self are defined as good or useful. Gratitude is good as well as are humiliation and apparently, at least sometimes, embarrassment.[200] The will *can be* good. It is good when used to work the Steps.

Working Steps Four and Five is not the end of guilt. With so much of the self defined as evil, the grouper will have much to feel guilty over without even counting overtly bad behavior. But he is still only beginning. Just recognizing all his defects takes Time.

As the grouper becomes more skilled at identifying more of himself as sinful or "defective" and learns to suppress awareness of the existence of these "bad/alcoholic/sinful" parts of himself, the subjective experience of an awareness of God is likely to increase. When "sharing" at a meeting, he may be surprised to find himself saying "spiritual" things he doesn't recognize as coming from himself. It is "God" speaking through him. Of course, he is merely repeating AA beliefs he has heard from other groupers, read in AA literature or knows "instinctively" because the dysfunctional beliefs responsible for his problem drinking are, to a large degree, held in common by other alcoholics. He has the *subjective experience* of God speaking through him because he is becoming less aware of his internal experience as he "turns over" his defects of character to God (uses thought-stopping techniques).

As the grouper learns that certain thoughts are

coming from his "Higher Power," he also learns that other thoughts and most emotions, those inconsistent with AA's definition of "good," are from the evil self which must be done away with. This "not AA" force, the self, is referred to as "my disease," "my alcoholic" or "John Barleycorn."

As the vital flow of information from the subconscious to the conscious becomes more restricted, Devil Drink assumes a mystical, magical, supernatural nature. Fear of the awesome power of Devil Drink, which is actually fear of oneself, intensifies dependence on Guidance from one's Higher Power. This Guidance is merely AA doctrine and the AA elders combined, perhaps, with the newly resurrected "abusive-parent-defined God."

Step Six: Were entirely ready to have God remove all these defects of character.

The Big Book version of how to work Step Six is extremely simple. One need only ask oneself if he is "willing" to have his "defects" removed. For defects he finds he would rather keep, he is to pray for the willingness to give them up.

Probably as a result of 13 years of practical AA experience, the 12 & 12's expanded discussion of this Step begins by cautioning the grouper not to expect much in the way of defect removal, "with most of them we shall have to be content with patient improvement."[201] Much of the discussion of this Step is about "lesser" sins, and about how everyone, if truly honest, can find many of them in themselves. After pointing out that most people don't steal, murder, rape, and be extremely lazy out of "self-interest, pure and simple,"[202] lesser degrees of these sins are pointed out. For instance, a lesser degree of stealing is letting "greed masquerade as ambition." For murder, which is caused by anger, a lesser degree would be "self-righteous anger." For rape, it would be "imaginary sex excursions." A milder version of being lazy is to work hard in order to retire.[203] Evidently Sun City, Arizona is Sin City. The intent of the comparison is to create guilt in the indoctrinee who has been working hard to retire or who has retired.

The goal of this Step is to further widen the definition of sin, to increase guilt, increase the need to purge that guilt and increase the feeling of a need to change. Most important of all, however, is the direction of this change. The grouper is to "become entirely willing to aim towards perfection."[204]

A popular AA cliché "Progress, not perfection" and an acknowledgement in Chapter Five of the Big Book that "We are not saints. ... We claim spiritual progress rather than spiritual perfection" would seem to be contradictory to "aiming towards perfection." However, Chapter Five and the slogan merely acknowledge that their ideal of perfection can't be reached. In AA, as in all mind control cults, an ahuman model of perfection is held out which is impossible to reach. The member is to always work to "progress." He is *never* done with the battle of suppressing his self. To achieve this "progress," the grouper is to "abandon limited objectives," meaning his own, "and move towards God's will for us,"[205] meaning AA objectives. The grouper, as with most non-hypnotic AA "suggestions," is cautioned, "Delay is dangerous, and rebellion may be fatal."[206]

Step Seven: Humbly asked Him to remove our shortcomings

The Big Book version of how to work Step Seven calls only for a simple prayer. The central theme of this prayer and this Step is, "I pray that you now remove from me every single defect of character which stands in the way of my usefulness to you and my fellows."[207]

The 12 & 12's expanded discussion stresses "humility" as "a necessary aid to our survival."[208] Against the threat of death without it, the newcomer is promised that, with humility, he has a good chance of "becoming truly happy,"[209] *in the future.** The major component of humility is "a desire to seek and to do God's will."[210] God's will, of course, is encompassed within the Steps. The path to humility is modeled by the elders' own journey. "But now the words, 'Of myself I am nothing, the Father doeth the works' began to carry bright promise and meaning."[211] This total discounting of each and every human being's innate value and God-given potential for growth and change is why AA members are so insistent that AA is responsible for, not only everything good in their lives, but also for life itself.

The supposition in this Step is that, if one is humble enough, God will remove one's "manifestations of self." It never occurs to the grouper that perhaps God created us as feeling, thinking beings for a reason. It does not occur to him that perhaps the AA elders don't have a special consciousness of God's will. If such thoughts surface, they are quickly dispelled. They would have long since been pointed out as the work of the "cunning, baffling, and powerful" one, the disease.

"Humility" is gradually acquired in AA. Each Step makes its own contribution. In Step One, the grouper admits he is "powerless" and is incompetent to manage his own life. He then admits he is insane, thoroughly discounts his own communication with God and comes to see himself as incompetent and evil and accepts that he can't change himself. In Step Seven, "humility," the discounting, holding in contempt and the disowning of

---

*All cults promise *future* reward for compliance with doctrine.

the self, is held up as an essential end in and of itself.

Before AA, the grouper drowned out selected parts of his self, his thoughts, emotions, awareness and potential, with alcohol. In AA, he intensifies his oppressive self-hatred with thought stopping techniques, adopting the "repentant sinner" role and telling others how sick he is. He ferrets out every aspect of self, redefining that which is "good" as coming from AA and that which is "bad" as being truly his.

Guilt arising from the existence of self leads the grouper into an orgy of "humble" confession. In this purging of guilt over being hopelessly defective, the grouper is no longer a lonely, wretched sinner. He is a wretched sinner with company. Everyone in a meeting suffers from pretty much identical defects even if some don't know it yet. By sharing his struggles, by confessing his "shortcomings," his "resentment," "self-pity," "willfulness," "alcoholic thinking" and "powerlessness," he momentarily purges the guilt of existence and feels as one with the group, the great moral crusade, with God.

Step Eight: Made a list of all persons we had harmed, and became willing to make amends to them all.

Step Nine: Made direct amends to such people wherever possible, except when to do so would injure them or others.

These Steps, like the others, mimic the spiritual principles of the world's great religions. However, in AA "making amends," elsewhere known as "atoning for one's sins," is also perverted. The major motivation for making amends in AA is not regret, but fear of drinking and dying. Also important is the promise of being "catapulted into the fourth dimension of existence" for "painstakingly" working the Steps.

This distorts the purpose behind acts of atonement. When a grouper makes amends, he isn't necessarily sorry. Of course, any act he does regret will make the list of Step Eight and amends will be made in Step Nine. However, he also is likely to "make amends" he wouldn't make if he valued his better judgment. In AA, if one's better judgment does not agree with the elders, it is merely "one's disease speaking." It is willfulness and self-centeredness.

This Step is often carried to ridiculous extremes. For example, one woman shared at a meeting that her sponsor had told her she must make amends in a situation where she had serious misgivings.

While alone in a ladies room, she was confronted by an a man standing in front of her masturbating. Shocked and frightened, she screamed at him to get out. He didn't blink. She screamed at him again. He still neither stopped nor left. Probably more out of panic than anything else, she hit him. Her sponsor told her that while what the man had done may have been wrong, it was her responsibility to "keep her own side of the street clean." She needed to make amends to him. Her "sobriety" was at stake.

While this example may seem extreme*, this woman's plight is not unusual in AA. It is entirely consistent with AA's view of the "alcoholic" as "bad child," sinner or hopeless defective. Doubtless her sponsor saw, and she

---

*The first AA member who criticized this as being an extreme example is a man who, as a child, was molested by a priest. In AA, he apologized to the priest for having been angry. I am also reminded of a woman who was gang raped. Her "spiritual advisors" tried to convince her it was her fault. Fortunately, she had sufficient sense of self to leave AA before being coerced into "making amends" to the rapists.

herself worried, that not wanting to make amends was a dangerous "manifestation of self." She was humiliated by the exhibitionist. If she actually carried out "making amends" she would have felt humiliated again. In AA, "humiliation = humility." It is a good emotion.

The final three Steps, Ten, Eleven and Twelve, can be called the "maintenance" Steps. Their purpose is to maintain the cult hold.

Step Ten: Continued to take personal inventory and when we were wrong promptly admitted it.

This Step is a call to continue the work of Steps Four through Nine in a regular, though perhaps less formal, manner. The inventory may be written or not and may be done daily, weekly or monthly. The important point is for the grouper to continue to ferret out instances where the self rears its ugly head. Any such finding is to be immediately followed by confession.

Step Eleven: Sought through prayer and meditation to improve our conscious contact with God as we understood Him, praying only for knowledge of His will for us and the power to carry that out.

In Step Eleven, the grouper is to work for "conscious contact." Rather than being an entirely new concept, it is more a continuation of Steps One, Two and Three. The call to pray "only for knowledge of God's will for us" means that one is not to pray "selfish" prayers. Essential to cult purposes, the answers that really come from God or one's Higher Power are consistent with AA doctrine, or at least with one's immediate elders.

When meditating,* one is to find a "good" thought to meditate upon. "We rest quietly with the thoughts of someone who knows, so that we may experience and learn."[212] This "good thought" may be given by one's sponsor. The general intent of this meditation is to "learn God's Will." However, whatever thoughts are used as a guide in meditation become firmly planted in the subconscious as unquestioned truth. Perhaps not by coincidence, this Step about searching for "conscious contact" and "praying for knowledge of God's Will" is immediately followed by a Step which answers those prayers. Step Twelve, from AA's point of view, is the ultimate expression of God's Will.

Step Twelve: Having had a spiritual awakening as the result of these steps, we tried to carry this message to alcoholics, and to practice these principles in all our affairs.

"Carrying the message" is the modern-day version of Oxford Group's Fifth C, Continuance. It has a much broader meaning than directly practicing conversion. The particular tasks of "carrying the message" are divided, although not by a sharp line, between the newcomers and the elders.

The newcomer is encouraged to "make a commitment" to help with the meetings by making coffee, setting up or cleaning up afterwards. For the newcomer, this is helping to "carry the message" since "rescuing the

---

*In my studies of hypnosis, I have found the only essential difference between a hypnotic trance and the meditative state is the source of the suggestions. In both, the "critical faculty" is diminished. Those accustomed to frequent meditation only need to be asked to "meditate" in order for them to quickly enter a hypnotic state even if they "have never been hypnotized before."

alcoholic who still suffers" is every group's "primary purpose." Doing the menial chores frees the elders to make their own efforts to carry the message. For an elder to get a newcomer to make such a commitment is also "carrying the message." This is usually done by telling him it will help keep him from drinking. The newcomer, although perhaps just emptying ashtrays, feels part of the great crusade to rescue the alcoholic who still suffers.

Newcomers are also expected to "take chips" and say a few words about how it wouldn't have been possible to acquire 30, 60 or 90 days of abstinence without AA. They are encouraged to share their trials and tribulations as a result of their disease. Confessions of shortcomings or difficulties are sympathetically heard and any credit given to AA is warmly applauded.

The reticent newcomer will be told how essential sharing is to "recovery." If the newcomer still won't budge, he may be given the suggestion that he could be dooming someone newer than himself for being so selfish. Rare is the individual who spends more than a few weeks going to meetings who doesn't get caught up in the orgy of confession and praise, pouring out his heart and soul to the congregation in sincere penance for his shortcomings and expressing deep gratitude to AA for salvation. In the eyes of those who are brand new, the "Fifth Step" sharing of the newer groupers is in stark contrast to the "Twelfth Step" sharing of the elders. The newcomer really is helping to carry the message. He is telling and showing how sick he is. People with Time, on the other hand, have already overcome the worst imaginable problems and no longer suffer from unpleasant emotions. The message is clear. Time in AA makes one "well."

The accumulation of Time changes the presentation given at the podium. As the "honeymoon period" wears off, the grouper finds that sharing anything other than how AA has made him "happy, joyous and free," or at the very least how AA is helping him progress, is received very coolly by the elder groupers.

As a person accumulates Time and works the Steps, he learns it is *selfish* to share about his problems. There are newcomers to be saved from certain jails, institutions and death. If his life isn't all he wants it to be, it's his fault. He obviously isn't working his Program well enough. Any "bad" feelings or thoughts are the work of Devil Drink. "My mind is telling me things are bad. Better to let God speak through me." It is wise and spiritual to "act as if." No point dooming others who have come for help.

There are many rewards for "carrying the message." Telling about how much the Program has helped is indirectly and "humbly" pointing out one's progress toward sanity and spiritual growth. There is also status in being a sponsor. But other reasons for "carrying the message" have more to do with avoiding punishment.

The most important driving force in AA is the fear of Devil Drink. AA considers its very existence and the survival of all members to Bill Wilson's revelation that an alcoholic needs another alcoholic (to save) in order to stay sober (saved). However, "giving that which was so freely given" is often used as a method of ignoring problems. The Big Book advises that "if sex is a problem, throw yourself all the more into helping others." Sponsors often advise their "babies," when they are having problems of any sort, to "help those less fortunate." In other words, the problems which were "dealt with" by drinking are now ignored by working to convince others that AA is the solution to their problems.

Another driving force behind the obsession to convert others was expressed by Oxford Group as "to keep the conversion experience real." It is typical of all totalitarian groups. The cult member is in a bind. No matter how well he was indoctrinated, he is always "in danger" of becoming aware of inconsistencies and having his whole world, a world based on the perfection of the doctrine, fall apart. He gets reassurance of the validity of the doctrine by convincing others. This is aptly called "the psychology of the pawn."

It is difficult to categorize the person who has been indoctrinated into AA. One thing that *can* be said about them, and that they will agree with, is that they do not drink moderately. While members are very vocal about having found "a solution to the alcohol problem," only a very small percentage of "true" alcoholics in AA, probably less than 5 percent, manage to *not* die from "their disease."* Most members go through seemingly random length periods of abstinence and then, *without having any real clue as to why*, set off on a suicidal drinking binge or even attempt suicide.** Many members "go in and out" for years and eventually give up on quitting drinking because they know that "AA is the last house on the block," meaning that if AA doesn't work there is nothing left to try.

Drinking by members is used to point out the dangers of "halfway measures" and as proof of how well the program works. The frequent suicides are passed off as "the alcohol got 'em" and serve as warnings to members to be humble, obedient, selfless and take direction from the elders who are further along the Spiritual Path.

In spite of the differences in those who have worked the Steps, there are many common characteristics...

---

*This is the number most often cited by members at meetings.

**I have kept some degree of contact with six of about twelve people in my "therapy" group four years ago. Three have attempted suicide. Two succeeded.

Chapter 12

Miracles of Recovery

Of the small percentage of those with significant exposure to AA who manage to remain abstinent, the vast majority continue to participate fully in cult activities, particularly "carrying the message" as speakers and sponsors.

A typical AA speaker is very adept at using confession to convince others of their own powerlessness, insanity, defectiveness and need for AA. The speaker often has motivations other than a sincere desire to help. It is doubtful the speaker is aware of them, since such awarenesses are inconsistent with being "spiritually awake" and would call for using thought-stopping techniques. I have never seen an AA member so transparent in this regard as a woman I'll call Debbie.

Debbie has almost 15 years of "sobriety." She was a prostitute in her younger days and uses this to great advantage when speaking. "Do you know what I used to do? I used to sell my ass. Yes, that's what I used to do." Her "humble confession," which is typical of elders in all mind-control cults, is something quite different. To quote Camus, "[I] ... practice the role of penitent to be able to end up as a judge ... the more I accuse myself, the more I have a right to judge you."

Debbie is different from the ordinary elder only in occasionally saying "you" to the congregation instead of always using "we" or "alcoholics." She tells them, "You may think you're the cream of the crop, but I'll tell you what you really are, you're the cream of the crap. You're sick. You're alcoholics." She continues at great length, always ending her tirades against "alcoholics," meaning all present, with a warm smile and "I love you all. Keep coming back." The congregation always responds with warm applause. She obviously does love them and very much. She "loves them enough to tell them the truth."

Another, more or less typical example of an AA alcoholic or "judge-penitent" is Georgia, a very popular speaker, not only because she has 35 years of Time, but because of the earthy "honesty" she has acquired during those years. The congregation is always awed by her "recovery." She has no reservations in labeling herself a sinner. She isn't at all guilty of "rationalizing" or "justifying" her behavior which would be symptomatic of "the disease." Her great recovery is clearly evident in her free confession of sin and defectiveness. Her story of alcoholic ruin and salvation by AA is frequently interspersed with, "I was (or am) nothing but a whore." Although she never was a prostitute, nor even particularly promiscuous, she did marry more than once. In AA, one can't be more "humble" or "honest" than putting one's past actions in the worst possible light. Her great humility and 35 years of Time testify to the Power of the Program. With her credentials established, she bears witness to the defects of all alcoholics. She is unrelenting in her indirect "we" and "alcoholics" judgements of the entire congregation.

These women benefit, as do all elders, from playing judge-penitent. To quote Robert J. Lifton, the worlds foremost authority on the "psychology of totalism,"* assuming this role,

> "becomes a vehicle for taking on some of the environment's arrogance and sense of omnipotence. Yet even this shared omnipotence cannot protect him from the opposite (but not unrelated) feelings of humiliation and weakness, feelings especially prevalent among those who remain more the enforced penitent than the all-powerful judge."[213]

In other words, in the AA environment, where the member is forced to acknowledge his "powerlessness," "insanity" and defectiveness, and to humiliate himself in other ways, he can feel less insane, defective, powerless and humiliated (feel "higher power") by merging himself with the all-powerful, sane, perfect Program and *becoming the humiliator*.

While AA speakers boast of how the Promises have been fulfilled, it has little relevance to their personal lives other than that they *probably* are not drinking or drugging.

Paul, for example, has been "sober" for over ten years. When speaking at meetings, he presents himself as entirely "together." "The Promises" have been fulfilled in his life. He not only had ten years of "sobriety," he had Serenity. When a friend of mine heard him speak, he was so impressed with Paul's "recovery" he asked him to be his sponsor. As it turned out, this paragon of AA virtue, absolutely abstinent and on "a spiritual path" for

---

*The psychology of totalism refers to the methods and psychology of "totalitarian groups." Among groups which can be considered totalitarian are the Red Chinese Communists, the Nazis, the parts of the Catholic Church involved in the Inquisition, the Moonies and Hari-Krishnas, and, of course, Alcoholics Anonymous.

more than ten years, is hardly a person who should be
"giving direction" of any kind, to anybody.

Paul still had serious problems and developed some
new ones he chose to avoid "confusing the newcomers"
with. He had no friends. He rarely left his apartment
except for AA meetings and spent most of his free time
alone with his television. He beat up his former male
lover so badly the man needed hospitalization. He also
was arrested for procurement in a public park. He has
become grossly overweight.

It is not unusual for people who quit an addiction
without dealing with the underlying problems to substitute another. It seems apparent that this man is now, in
Twelve Step jargon, "using" sex, food and perhaps
television. He may also be held up as an example of the
dangers of "turning over" his anger to his "higher power."
In plain English, "turning it over" is repressing it.

It may be difficult to imagine how he can justify the
difference between his personal life and the one he
presents from the podium but, having adopted the
"spiritual principle" of "Powerlessness," the quality of his
life has little to do with him. He's powerless. The
bumper sticker on his car bears the AA slogan, "SHIT
HAPPENS."

Scores of examples can be cited of people with Time
beginning, or continuing, to do things destructive to
themselves or others, but such characterizations don't
prove anything except that such people exist. An AA
member would respond that they had problems before
they came to AA which is undoubtedly true. The important point is the credibility of the "AA successes." Are
those who have worked the Twelve Steps "miracles of
mental health" as they claim? Do they have a special
knowledge or wisdom about alcoholism?

One interesting and celebrated example of what

"recovery" is all about is the story of Kitty Dukakis. Kitty Dukakis is a self-described alcoholic, addict and manic-depressive. She has been hospitalized several times over eight years and has lectured on addiction and alcoholism with the intention of helping others. She has written an autobiography, "Now You Know." Her story, other than her husband's race for the presidency, is far from unique in AA.

She was raised by a mother who had serious problems of her own. By Kitty Dukakis's own account, some very destructive lessons were taught to, and well learned by, young Kitty. Some of the messages she was given were: you have no personality, you're less than the "red weasel" (red weasel was the nickname given her sister because she was thought to be so ugly), you are the cause of my rage, you are to be perfect, you are not worthy of praise, if others should compliment you it is meaningless, you can never win an argument and, by example, it is bad to have fun.

Her father appears to have been more indirect. He is described as "plagued by self-doubt,"[214] and cryptically referred to as "...naturally makes everyone around him feel good, even when he's punishing them."[215] He also had a strange sense of humor. He liked to introduce his two young daughters saying "one is much better than the other" and let the two little children figure out who.[216] Her father was also a practical joker.[217] When she got her first job in a record store, on her first day at work, he called and asked her for Beethoven's Tenth. She spent hours looking for it. As Kitty told it,

> "'You dimwit,' laughed my dad, 'Beethoven only wrote nine symphonies.'
>
> Dad pulled stunts like that on me the whole time I worked

there. He always liked to make people laugh."[218]

It seems strange that a father would play that kind of prank on his insecure daughter's first day at work. Was he giving the message that she was stupid or incompetent? Was he, like when he was overtly punishing, making her enjoy it? Was he merely amusing himself and his friends at his daughter's expense? Or was it, as humor often is, a veiled way of expressing hostility?

Her father's humor and punishment could well have been "crazy-making." A father who works to make a child "feel good" when being punished is putting the child in a terrible bind. A small child feels bad when he has displeased a parent. A parent who builds the expectation in the child that not "feeling good" while being punished will further disappoint the parent teaches the child an extremely destructive lesson. The child's only available conclusion, since the parent must be held as right, is "my feelings are bad." The same goes for when a child is the butt of a parent's jokes if the parent expects the child to enjoy it. To be angry at being ridiculed is "bad." The small child again concludes, "my feelings are bad." The child learns to suppress the feelings in an attempt to be "good." The child may even learn to "feel good" when being punished, or to "enjoy" being ridiculed. But, out of sight, and out of the conscious mind of the obedient child, the anger and rage boil away.

While there is no way to be certain of the exact nature of the destructive lessons she learned as a child, Kitty Dukakis makes it very clear how she felt:

> "My childhood was stacked with remorse; most of the time I walked around feeling I'd done something wrong. I lived under a Damoclean sword of accusation, and at any given moment it could drop and cut off, if not my head, my confidence."[219]

It was accepted by her mother that Kitty had one thing going for her though it wasn't something she should feel good about. Unlike the "red weasel," she was attractive. In her teen years, she began gaining weight, and thereby losing the only thing she was allowed to value in herself. Following her mother's example, she began taking diet pills. Her mother disapproved of her "boundless energy" and "talking too much" and warned her to stop. However, she didn't quit. She took one a day for the next 26 years.

After only a few weeks the body develops tolerance and, for all practical purposes, the pills no longer have an appreciable physical effect.* However, there may have been important psychological reasons for taking them.

Kitty Dukakis was living "under a Damoclean sword of accusation." She constantly felt guilty over what she might have done or would do. As long as she took diet pills, the pills were responsible, at least in her own mind, for her behavior. She was free to be talkative, active and "silly." As long as she took the pills she had permission. One of her coping methods was to stay busy, "I could run away from my thoughts, from my feelings, and from my fears."[220] Believing the pill-a-day would keep her active and being able to attribute any "silliness" or imperfection resulting from her activity to "the drug," it is easy to imagine that it was an effective, though far from productive, way of coping with life.

In telling of her 26 years of "drug addiction," Kitty D. writes the history of an "addict" from the Twelve Step

---

*This is not to say that discontinuance would not have caused transitory discomfort but that due to the body's adjustment, one wouldn't be, after continued use of a small amount of a drug, appreciably more "energetic" or "talkative" or *anything else* due to *pharmacological* effects. After taking her daily pill, she would only feel as she would have if she had never taken them.

point of view. She has no real "horror story" of what "the drugs made me do." She tells of the events in her life, unhappy first marriage, pregnancy, divorce and later remarriage, from the perspective that the diet-pill-a-day was somehow extremely relevant. "In December of 1956, I started using,"[221] "I was still taking my morning pill,"[222] "Only one thing had remained constant throughout those four years, my addiction."[223]

As a Twelve Stepper, Kitty D. looks at her past in terms of what the drug did:

> "We had some tough moments, times when I would fly off the handle to such an extent that Michael would wind up not speaking to me. Of course he didn't know it was the pills talking."[224]

Perhaps we are to believe that, just like the little girl in the Exorcist, Kitty Dukakis was seized by a demon and forced, against her will, to say rageful things to her husband, that it wasn't her talking. Perhaps she wasn't ever, in those 26 years, ever angry at anyone.

But maybe anger was one of the feelings she ran from. Maybe she felt guilt over her natural, normal human response. Maybe, during the years she spent running to keep it out of her awareness, her anger grew into an ever more frightening rage. Maybe it sometimes caught up with her, but she had worked so successfully at ignoring it she couldn't recognize it as her own. Or maybe it was just easier to pretend it wasn't hers.

Whatever the case, while "using" she attributed all good she did to the pills, "[E]verything I accomplished during that quarter of a century plus I attributed to the chemicals ruling my body. I actually felt that without them, none of these achievements would have been possible."[225] It seems but a small step to do the same with all that she disapproved of in herself.

Her "bottom" as an "addict" was at her daughter's eighth grade graduation. As Kitty D. confesses, "I was talking loudly and snapping." "I squirmed in my seat." Knowing her behavior was "indefensible," and attributing it to the diet pill, she took action.

After 26 years of suffering an "addiction" which made her basically no different from anyone else, Kitty Dukakis got "help." She spoke to her brother-in-law, who had "always been open about his own alcoholism and subsequent recovery."* Kitty Dukakis, in July of '82, was in treatment for drug addiction.

Kitty D. claims that during her 28-day, AA-based treatment she was helped. "I accepted the fact that I was addicted to pills." Taking her words at face value opens the question of how "accepting" what she must already have believed to enter treatment was help. The "acceptance of her addiction" actually means she took the first Step and accepted AA/treatment center doctrine on the nature of addiction: that she was "powerless" and her life was "unmanageable."

She was advised she was also an alcoholic in spite of the fact that she didn't have a drinking problem. While in treatment, Kitty D. was expected to identify herself as an addict and alcoholic. In spite of being warned she was also an alcoholic, it seems that Kitty's "disease told her" she was only an addict. After treatment, she refused to identify herself at meetings as an alcoholic. She would only say, "My name is Kitty and I am an addict."

---

*While nothing is said in her autobiography about the brother-in-law convincing her that her less-than-perfect behavior was due to the daily diet pill or that he had been working on her to convince her of the need for help, the statement "had always been open about his own alcoholism" does imply he was "fishing" for a convert. As a grouper he would have felt a moral obligation to "help." "Through confession we may win his soul."

Her problem with identifying herself as an alcoholic
was based in the fact that she didn't have a drinking
problem. Her "chronology of alcoholism," up to this point,
was getting sick once from two glasses of spiked punch in
high school; getting sick once from "a few too many" in
college and getting sick from drinking one Zombie in
Mexico during her first marriage. These three instances
were in her distant past.

After leaving treatment, she remained abstinent from
both pills and alcohol and attended "support group
meetings." She also began eight years of depression
which she attributes, of course, to the pills. Believing the
pills enabled her to be active and run at a safe distance
from her feelings, she may well have felt "helpless"
without them. AA taught her she is powerless, insane,
has "bad" feelings and that being angry can kill her. If
having her crutch taken away wasn't enough to bring on
depression, it is easy to imagine that AA indoctrination
was.

Kitty D. was soon on drugs again, but this time, the
kind psychiatrists prescribe.* After a few months she
quit going to meetings and began drinking moderately.
However, she continued to lecture as an authority, "as
one who knows," on drugs and addiction.

She managed fairly well over the next few years. She
didn't have a drinking problem. She involved herself in
numerous activities. Everything seemed to be going fine
until April, 1987 when Michael Dukakis formally announced his run for the presidency.

The campaign trail is extremely stressful. As the wife

---

*She was seeing a psychiatrist who was "in recovery" himself. To
quote an early psychiatric "friend" of AA, a Dr. Harry M. Tiebout, the
therapist's job is "breaking down the patient's inner resistance [to AA]
so that which is inside him will flower ... under the activity of the
A.A. program."

of the presidential contender, she had to give up her own work and interests. She had to hand over the management of her life to staff assistants who told her when to get up, when and where to eat, where to go, who to talk to, what to say, what not to say and when and where to sleep. Her day began at 5:30 am and ended around 2 am. Duties included speaking to groups, answering questions and, perhaps most importantly, always being "up" for the ever-present cameras. There was never a moment's privacy. Great care was taken in everything she said and did. A mere slip of the tongue on her part could cost her husband the presidency.

Such a schedule would quickly take a toll on anyone but Kitty Dukakis had two additional strikes against her.

First of all, she didn't like herself; she felt like a fake. Being constantly under the watchful eye of the cameras must have been terrifying. Someone might see who she thought she really was. The other was that, in the treatment center, "the seed had been planted." As Kitty tells it, "Buried way back in my brain was a warning I had received at the Hazelden Clinic back in 1982." The warning, perhaps better termed "AA suggestion," was that she was an alcoholic and would *eventually* "lose control."

At the end of each day, the campaign team got together to relax over drinks. Kitty joined in. During the entire campaign, she had one drink a day. The entire staff looked forward to the end of the work day, to being able to kick back and finally relax out of the glare of the TV cameras and have a drink. Kitty, however, with the seed firmly planted, felt as though something was wrong with her to look forward to that drink. She knew alcohol's power. It was Devil Drink that was good about the end of the day. Being out of the spotlight, having the pressure off, being able to relax and socialize, being able to be herself without ruining anyone's career were irrelevant. It was Devil Drink that made her feel better.

The two-year campaign ended with Michael Dukakis's loss. Kitty, having given up much of what was important to her, had nothing to fall back on. She had even quit her antidepressants. Even worse, during the entire campaign, she had dealt with the stress by working even harder. She ran from her feelings and, as they threatened to overwhelm her and disrupt the all-important presidential race, she ran even faster. Now, with the campaign over, with nowhere to run, Kitty soon caught up with Kitty.

The dynamics of Kitty D.'s two-month drinking career may be evident to the reader of her book, although perhaps not clear to her.

Kitty D. virtually dropped all outside activity. In her inner world, she battled with great success against "negative" thoughts and feelings. Loss of the election and whatever else was or wasn't going on in her life *called for* such thoughts and feelings. Since she had given up much of what was important to her, what made her feel good, she was left with *nothing* on the inside. "I was faced with a gaping emptiness I could not endure."[226]

Normally a person recovers from such a situation in time since sooner or later their feelings catch up with them. But Kitty D. knew from "treatment" that she was suffering symptoms peculiar to the disease of alcoholism. From her campaign experience, she knew alcohol had a special power to make her feel good. In treatment, she must have heard countless stories of the great painful emptiness peculiar to the alcoholic. She also knew, since the seed had been so firmly planted, what she could and was expected of her to do to fix it. She could drink. She must also have known, at least in the back of her mind, that she would end up in treatment again. Perhaps being in a hospital is what she wanted more than alcohol because it didn't take her long to get there.

While it is difficult to follow the number and dates of all her treatments, she seems to have gone through shorter and shorter periods of relative stability. The last self-destructive incident she reported was drinking hair spray, again resulting in treatment.

Her last AA-based treatment, like the previous ones, had its effect on Kitty D. In her 1982 treatment, she "accepted" she was an addict, the seed was planted that she was an alcoholic, and she began suffering depression. In early 1989, she "accepted" her alcoholism and began a series of extremely self-destructive acts. In late 1989, she got further help. Now the outside observer might conclude that the help she had been getting seriously aggravated her problems. This is "unspiritual thinking." The Program is perfect. There merely was something more wrong with Kitty D., something which she "accepted" in her most recent treatment.

Kitty D. is a manic-depressive. That means that she *must be* on drugs, not merely one diet pill a day, but lithium. So now Kitty D., recovering alcoholic, addict and manic depressive, has finally acquired the promised Serenity. She has been given "The Keys to the Kingdom:" the Twelve Steps of Alcoholics Anonymous *and a bottle of highly potent pills.*

Between hospitalizations, Kitty D. kept busy educating others about addiction and alcoholism. She still wants to carry the message. She is planning to visit the Soviet Union to give them that which she was so freely given.

Chapter 13

How Far Carried?

AA has been much more successful than the Oxford Group. In its heyday, Oxford reached more than 60 countries. AA is active in more than 114. To understand this phenomenal growth one must understand the nature and purpose of "not AA" organizations.

To keep AA purely spiritual, the membership has what appears to be severe restrictions on efforts to "carry the message." They can't solicit or accept money from outside sources. They can't ally themselves, as a group, with other organizations. They must, as AA members, remain anonymous in the media. As AA members, they can't take a public stand on any political or social issue. However, there are no restrictions on AA members *founding* outside organizations allied with AA or moving existing organizations into alliance with AA. As members of outside organizations they are able to solicit funds and take stands on social and political issues. They can also "educate the public." In fact a "not AA" corporation can do whatever it sees fit to "carry the message" except use the AA name and identify itself with the public as AA. In a legal, corporate sense, AA doctrine has been spread more by "not AA" organizations and "not AA" people than by AA.

The most innocuous of these "not AA" organizations are the corporations operating AA clubhouses. Major cities have many locations operated, staffed and used exclusively by AA members* for meetings and socializing. These clubhouses are "not AA." In keeping with The Traditions, mixing "property and prestige" with the "spiritual" is not allowed. AA would never ask for or accept money from outside sources but AA members can band together to establish "not AA" clubhouses. These "not AA" corporations solicit public money for the needs of "people in recovery from alcoholism and drug addiction," not for AA.

Another "not AA" organization is the publicly funded treatment center. They are managed and staffed by AA members and the "treatment" offered is AA indoctrination but it is "not AA." Being "not AA," they are free to solicit public funds.

This represents only a small part of AA's influence which begins with their approach to medicine and religion. The individual AA member, even though he humbly knew he was more capable of helping alcoholics than either doctors or ministers, was advised in the 1939 Big Book to "cooperate; never criticize."[227]

Religious and medical organizations were frustrated in their attempts to get excessive drinkers to moderate or quit. AA members, boasting of a personal "cure" for the "disease," found fertile ground. Indoctrinated members, whether they drank or not, agreed on the nature of the disease. Those who were abstinent at the moment pointed to "a simple program" as the cause of their success. Those who continued to drink or who's drinking became worse could point to their own willfulness, stubbornness, self-centeredness or lack of honesty for their failure and praise AA for their sincere desire to help. Those only partially indoctrinated, who didn't want

---

*They may share the facilities with other Twelve Step groups.

to continue going to AA, were explained by co-founder Wilson. "Initial rejection of A.A. is part of the denial mechanism."[228] Against this background, it was difficult to be critical of AA. Those associated with AA were full of praise for it and those who didn't like it were suffering a disease symptom. Casual observation showed sincere, successful people trying to help others and themselves.

AA has neutralized almost all criticism from organized religion. With AA's stress on a "higher power," the early suggestion that members affiliate with a church and the insistence that it is a "spiritual, not religious" program, most religious organizations were swayed and remain so today. It would have been extremely difficult for a religious leader to criticize AA. His main awareness of AA was through new members attributing church attendance, and the solution of serious problems, to a new-found awareness of God brought about by AA. It would also be difficult for a religious organization to criticize AA when AA is apparently so full of praise for religious organizations.

It is difficult for a non-member to catch the hidden criticisms of other religions in AA literature. For example, in the AA book "Pass It On," Bill Wilson's thoughts on religion are given:

> "The ungodly might not be expected to know any better. But men of religion should. Yet history shows that they just don't. It seems to me that the great religions survive because each has a sound core of spirituality. They survive because of their spirituality..."[229]

The casual reader would find a lukewarm defense of religion; they have "a sound core of spirituality" which outweighs "history." However, the indoctrinated cult member is aware that organized religion is good to the degree it has the pure substance of AA. AA is purely spiritual and not at all religious. AA requires no beliefs. Beliefs are essential to religion. AA doesn't need to require beliefs because those who don't "come to believe" their beliefs will die. This means AA is the pure embodiment of what allows organized religion to be *somewhat good* and that AA is more powerful and has a more direct line to God. AA also has no "history" other than that "[O]ur [AA's] world arteries ... carry the life-giving grace of God."[230] Ironically, only a few fringe religious groups, with techniques similar to those of AA, are able to recognize them and warn their members. Apparently, the only religious groups which have been vocal in their criticism of AA are some of the more extreme Fundamentalist Christian groups. There is now a Twelve Step organization to "help those addicted" to them, Fundamentalists Anonymous.

AA's modern relationship with other religions can be summed up by a conversation overheard at an AA meeting among a half-dozen or so groupers,

"Did you read the article that said AA was taking the place of religion?" Some groupers indicated they had. "She shouldn't have said it," he continued. "But it's true," one grouper protested. "Yeah but she still shouldn't have said it." All heads nodded in agreement.

While AA has been extremely successful in its relationship with most religions, its influence on medicine has been much greater. Some members of the medical establishment are among its greatest boosters. A doctor who has been indoctrinated into AA or Al-Anon can not speak "at the media level" about alcoholism *as an AA*. That would be "breaking Anonymity." He can, however, "carry the message" as *a medical authority*.

In the medical school text, "The Treatment of Alcoholism," the student is taught,

"Every effort should be made to introduce the patient to AA. Schedules of local AA meetings should be kept in the office and given to each patient. The physician should know several recovered men and women active in local AA who are willing to meet with a new patient, share their experiences, and take the patient to an AA meeting."[231]

If the excessive drinker would rather quit on his own, the doctor is to suggest that the person who tries to quit "by himself ... usually fails"[232] *as if people who go to AA have a lower failure rate.* The psychiatrist is advised that his "primary goal" is to establish a "therapeutic relationship" with the patient in order to use it as "leverage" to get him into AA.[233]

None of this is surprising since the book is written with the admitted goal of getting people into AA[234] by a man who got his information from the "insights" of "recovered" alcoholics, going to AA meetings and friendships with AA groupers.[235] The author claims "a deeper understanding of alcoholism, an understanding that is not approached by the usual process of medical education."[236]

This medical textbook and its acceptance would not have been possible without the AMA declaring alcoholism a disease in 1956. Based upon the faulty work of E.M. Jellinek,* a disease of alcoholism defined as incurable, progressive, characterized by "denial" and fatal without "help" has medical legitimacy.

This declaration was made with the best of intentions. Undoubtedly, some imagined the results would be alcoholics getting effective treatment and a major impact on the nation's alcohol problems. The results, however, have been entirely different. While there has been no decrease in alcoholism attributable to its being classified

---

*see Chapter 3, "Disease Theory"

as a disease, there has been a dramatic increase in the growth of AA.

With alcoholism an officially sanctioned disease, states began forcing insurers to pay for treatment creating the multi-billion-dollar treatment industry. The treatment offered was, and still is, unproven, ineffective, AA indoctrination.

The ramifications go much further: *AA has become America's quasi-official religion.* While there has been great public discussion over many church-state issues, an increasing portion of the federal government's budget has gone to pay for Twelve Step indoctrination under the guise of treatment. The 1991 federal budget alone calls for almost *four billion dollars* for "treatment." State, county and city governments, at the urging of "those who know," each contributes its own share.

With almost one and a half million people going through treatment every year, there has been no decrease in alcoholism or drug addiction rates. There has, however, been a great increase in the power and influence of Twelve Step groups.

Governmental agencies, particularly the courts, routinely coerce people into AA indoctrination. The choice is frequently AA or jail in spite of research which shows that coercion into AA/treatment increases problem drinking.[237]

Members in good standing of the Moonies, as almost any other cult, don't have alcohol or drug problems, regardless of their status before indoctrination. What would be the public's response if this year's budget called for four billion dollars for indoctrination centers for the Moonies or Hari-Krishnas? The only real differences between these groups and AA is that they are honest about being religious groups and, at least with the Moonies, members moderate rather than abstain.

AA has also been extremely successful with the mass media. Rarely, if ever, is a story even slightly critical of AA ever published or shown on television. The media instead reports successful "recovery."

Typical of television news was Los Angeles station KCAL's special report on alcoholism. The report claimed there are an estimated 22 million alcoholics in the United States with another 82 million affected by the alcoholics. "If left untreated alcoholism, like other addictions, gets progressively worse" the report warned. A Twelve Step cult member then gave evidence of how alcohol nearly destroyed her and how treatment saved her.

An alcoholism treatment expert from a local hospital-based treatment center explained, in "outsider doctrine," what AA is,

> "It's a real simple program of fellowship. The Twelve Steps involve working with other people, being honest with other people and learning to accept help from outside of themselves."

Listeners were given the number of Alcoholics Anonymous for more information. The newscaster thanked the researchers who "only wanted to help" for the report.

Television and movies invariably show alcoholic characters in the AA disease theory mold. They suffer the consequences of, and all their "bad behavior" is attributable to, their "disease" until saved by AA. In a recent episode of "Beverly Hills 90210," one of the main characters, a teenage boy, threw a party while his parents were out of town, got drunk and wrecked the family car. The situation was resolved when a warm, understanding, wiser teenager, who had "lived it," brought him to an AA meeting. He went home with acceptance of his alcoholism and, presumably, lived responsibly ever after. No mention was made of a lifetime commitment to attend meetings, an obsession to get others to join, the rest of the family being sick and needing "help" or any other aspect of AA "spirituality."

Television dramas and sitcoms give the impression that once joining AA, drinking problems, presented as the source of all problems, are solved almost as simply as just remembering "One Day at a Time." Never do the rigors of indoctrination result in a return to drinking. The pressures people are put under to change their concepts of God and accept the Big Book as divinely inspired are not shown. The mass media never presents characters, real or fictional, who drink more or who commit suicide following AA involvement.

According to the Big Book, Bill Wilson was planning to save the entire world as far back as 1938. One early AA member said Bill Wilson and another early member "were not only going to save all the drunks in the world but also the so-called normal people!"[238]

Their humble plans are being fulfilled.

The major difference between Oxford Group and AA is that AA concentrates efforts at indoctrination on only those with one "spiritual disease." Oxford Group members knew they needed to save others, any others, in order to stay saved. AA members know that only saving other alcoholics will keep them saved.

Many AA members soon found that, even if they managed to not drink, other addictive behaviors became problems. Since they attributed the Twelve Steps to their not drinking, forming Twelve Step groups for these other addictions seemed logical. This was first done for other chemical addictions with the founding of Pills Anonymous, Narcotics Anonymous, Cocaine Anonymous and Marijuana Anonymous among others. It has spread to cover non-chemical addictions with groups like Gamblers Anonymous. These groups all center about the "proven" Twelve Steps. In Step One, the word "alcohol" is replaced with the appropriate object of addiction. In Step Twelve, "alcoholics" is replaced with "addicts" or "compulsive gamblers."

Members of Gamblers Anonymous follow the same pattern as AA members in their efforts to "carry the message." A recent PBS program, "Lucky Number," used "recovering" people and treatment industry figures as experts on compulsive gambling. The first part of the program featured a "recovering" gambler who explained compulsive gambling. "I needed to gamble just like the drug addict needed to put a needle in their arm." Statistics were presented to show the seriousness of the problem.[*]

The fact that there are only 26 treatment centers for compulsive gamblers was lamented. A treatment center employee claimed a success rate of 85 percent with Gamblers Anonymous[**]. The only question deemed worthy of discussion was who should pay for more "treatment," the gaming industry or the government.

The Twelve Step religion has spread to almost every group of people who are vulnerable due to suffering any disease, illness or problem which has a high rate of natural remission. It has even spread to people who have

---

[*]Compulsive gambling is a serious problem and growing worse with more states legalizing various forms of gambling and even running promotional campaigns showing the state lotteries as *a solution to problems and source of wealth and joy.*

[**]The success rate was "for those who follow aftercare." There was no definition of success and no evidence was given for the seriousness of the individual cases. No figures were given for those who didn't follow aftercare and nothing was said about the nature of aftercare. In a 1988 study of Gamblers Anonymous only 7 percent remained abstinent from gambling for two years. See Stewart and Brown (1988)

no particular problem except that they are normal human beings. Groups have been formed for schizophrenia, depression and mental illness in general. Other groups have been formed for people who eat too much, cheat on their spouses, have too much sex, mismanage their money, have cancer, are homosexuals and are Fundamentalist Christians. Many programs have parallel programs for family and friends who are, of course, sick too. There are now more than 100 different Twelve Step programs each with its own particular "disease" used as leverage for conversion.

These are casually referred to as "support" groups. Even though most of them deal with temporary "diseases," or only with spouses or friends of those with the "diseases," none accepts that people can ever get well and leave. They all call for lifetime dedication to the Steps, meetings and converting others.

For instance, a depressed person may be told he needs a support group. If he goes to what one generally imagines is a support group, he will receive help and understanding from others who are learning to deal with their depression. Members will leave when they no longer feel the need for special support. The Twelve Step "support" group, however, will make every effort to convince the person he is powerless, insane, incompetent, the group is God and he must "work the program one day at a time." If he asks how long before he is well and can leave, he may be told that worrying about such things is a disease symptom and must be repressed. If the depressed person doesn't "get well," he may be told it is because he isn't "working with others." He'll be happy only if he convinces others that they'll become happy by joining the group.

The newest Twelve Step program is the most inclusive. It is for a newly recognized "disease" suffered by, according to one authority, 96 percent of the population because of the way they were raised. According to another authority, the 4 percent who weren't raised under those conditions are sick from having to live in this world with the rest of us. This new "disease," from which *everyone* suffers, is codependency. The spiritual program where one must go to recover from this "sometimes fatal malady" is Codependents Anonymous, familiarly known as Coda.

The authorities on codependency do not quite agree on a definition although they agree most everyone has it and would benefit from joining Coda. A non-member, Alan Marlatt of the Addictive Behaviors Research Center at the University of Washington, defines codependency quite sarcasticly and accurately as "what used to be called caring for others."[239] The "Codependency Movement" holds that codependents, in not understanding their powerlessness, make their lives unmanageable by always trying to please and help others. This is the root of the most widely accepted definition, relationship addiction. The symptoms include, but are not limited to, feeling sad, angry, disappointed, rejected, lonely or abandoned at the end of a relationship or not wanting a relationship to end.

There are many symptoms directly related to romantic involvement but "the disease" takes other forms, the most cunning and baffling perhaps being *not being involved* romantically. Other symptoms of the disease are working as a nurse, doctor, therapist or in any of the helping professions. People pick these professions because of their disease. While perhaps not everyone in these professions is sick, most show obvious symptoms. They become upset when a patient dies, commits suicide or does poorly in any other way. Codependents get upset when they can't "control" other people by helping them.

The solution to codependency, of course, is the Twelve Steps. In Step One, "so-called normal people" are to admit they are "powerless over others," that they can't really help anyone and must give up their "rescuer" role. In Step Twelve, they are to go out and dedicate themselves to rescuing everyone they can by getting them to join Coda.

Codependents Anonymous is split between two seemingly opposing membership factions. One is "traditional AA." The other is made up of people who hold many of the characteristics of the "traditional AA" but have a therapist who is a grouper or are therapists themselves. The second faction blends modern psychology with the "old time religion" of AA. Which faction takes precedence is quickly obvious at any meeting. At the "traditional" meetings, the sharing is characterized by "I am *so* sick that..." In the generally upper-middle-class "psychological" meetings, the sharing is characterized by pseudo-psychological phrases like "my inner child" and "dysfunctional family."

The suggested reading lists highlight this split. "Twelve Steps and Twelve Traditions" appears on the same list as pop psychology bestsellers on codependency. As yet, they have no Big Book.

Coda's indoctrination techniques are more varied and, in many ways, more clever than AA's. The "traditional" faction is more likely to use fear. "The disease kills." The "psychology" faction adds newer, more sophisticated methods. Many of Coda's founders are trained psychologists who, having "recovered" in AA, thought that there must be another disease since they had gained no Serenity. Once they found codependency, they set to work with skills adopted from modern psychology to carry the message.

The most potent techniques fall under the blanket phrase "work with the inner child." Some of these techniques were used on the television talk show, "Sally Jessy Raphael." Guest John Bradshaw, 25 years "in recovery" from alcoholism and codependency and a guru of the codependency movement, did some "demonstrations" for the television audience. The most powerful was a hypnosis session in which the home audience was invited to participate.

The audience was instructed to close their eyes and go back to the earliest house they lived in as a child. "Notice the detail of it..." Suggestions were given to see one's mother and father and then "find the little child you once were." The suggestions were designed to bring into focus any childhood conflicts one may have had with one's parents.

> "Tell him [the child you once were] 'I know what you've been through.' Look at your Mom and Dad and tell them you have to leave now because you have to have a life of your own. I am no longer going to carry your pain for you. I am no longer going to be an extension for your ambition. I have a right to my own life."

The messages given here are obvious: you (as a child) had unpleasant experiences and it was Mom and Dad's fault. They wouldn't let you have a life of your own, they expected you to carry their pain and they made you an extension of their ambition. Under hypnosis, a person will do his best to make the suggestions real. Appropriate unpleasant childhood memories are tied to the suggestions.

The next step in the hypnotic session was the separation of a person from "Mom and Dad." The audience was given the suggestion to "Start walking away, you and that child." As the audience "leaves Mom and Dad," their replacement becomes apparent. "You and this child can... have your own life. If you don't have a support group in your life tell your child, 'I'll get you one, a new family of affiliation.'" Needless to say, it would be difficult for someone to find a support group or "new family of affiliation" for "my inner child" that isn't Codependents Anonymous.

The session ended with a typical hypnotic suggestion to "Go to the most special place you know" to leave the hypnotic subjects, no matter what emotional turmoil they may have been through, "feeling good" and wanting to repeat the experience.

With the birth of codependency, everyone is sick, insane and in need of "a spiritual program." It is the disease of "so-called normal people." *Everyone needs to be saved.*

With the combined membership of all Twelve Step groups, there are now between 10 and 15 million believers dedicated to "carrying the message" in America. While the phenomena of the Twelve Step cults might seem unique, not too long ago a similar group with nearly identical techniques shocked the Western world.

Upon the release of Western civilians held in Red Chinese prisons in the mid-1950s, it was found that some of them kept "repeating their false confessions, insisting upon their guilt, praising the 'justice' and 'leniency' which they have received, and expounding the 'truth' and 'righteousness' of all Communist doctrine."[240] Most shocking to the American public was that many of these had been Christian missionaries. The press made much of "brainwashing" and torture but careful investigation found that those who were tortured, or even saw others severely mistreated at the hands of the communists, didn't convert. The common thread among those who did convert was that they all believed in the *sincerity* of the communist authorities and their cellmates. They believed that they were sincerely trying to *help*.

The Chinese communists, unlike their Russian mentors, had a program of "re-education" for "reactionaries." Most of this re-education was voluntary, but the more severe reactionaries needed "intervention." Among these were Westerners, mostly missionaries, who had stayed in China after the revolution.

The re-education of these "reactionaries" parallel those of the American alcoholic coerced into "treatment."* The experience of "thought reform" in the Chinese population at large directly parallels that of the American alcoholic who voluntarily enters "treatment." The "treatment modality" is the same. In both situations, people are removed from any positive support for their identity and are "educated" by a unanimous majority about the nature of their disease. The new prisoner or patient is to confess and accept his identity as a diseased person in need of "cure." He is no longer a doctor, businessman or priest. He is a "reactionary" or "alcoholic." A prisoner's or patient's peers, having admitted their own disease, are absolutely sincere and know the importance of helping. Having been helped themselves, they know how to proceed. "Errors in thinking and judgement" and "alcoholic thinking" are pointed out. As the indoctrinee begins to see the world and himself from the viewpoint of his peers, he begins to see his own guilt and identifies himself as a guilty person.

The guilt one comes to feel is not so much over being a "reactionary" or "alcoholic" in the usual senses of the words. It is over one's existence as a non-believer as defined by the doctrine. For instance, the "reactionary" or "alcoholic" who worked hard in order to retire sees himself as *guilty of selfishness and self-centeredness*. He

---

*It isn't much different from the Oxford Group program and their "hospital work" either. One poor soul, a prisoner who was a Protestant minister and had been a grouper, was reindoctrinated by the communists. He reports he "was struck by its similarity with the Moral Rearmament [Oxford Group] movement."

didn't work for the cause. He was only concerned with himself. The "spy" or "alcoholic" who did what he once considered unselfish things learns he was in the service of evil. The missionary who helped feed and clothe the poor is now guilty of "deceiving the people" by making "reactionary forces" look good. The grouper who bought a hungry man lunch is guilty of "enabling."

Perhaps the most motivating form of guilt in terms of identity change is guilt arising from disappointing "those who are only trying to help." The emotional attachments can be quite intense in both the thought reform and the alcoholism treatment center environments. Special meetings foster these attachments. In China they are called "struggle meetings." In the U.S. they are called the "hot seat." In this "therapeutic technique," a recalcitrant "sick" person is chosen for special attention. His peers, in order to help him, tell him, in the strongest terms, how unlikable, sinful and useless he is. While this "therapy" sometimes results in psychotic reactions, the intent is to cure, not destroy. The effect is to shake a person's sense of identity enough to create a desperate need for positive confirmation. To get this from his peers, he must adopt the "repentant sinner" role. He will also develop closer emotional ties with those who were harshly critical but now are willing to help by being understanding. At the very least, he is more willing to accept help from those "more advanced" in order to avoid another struggle session.

"Re-education" also includes a written confession identical to AA's Step Four. In writing his confession, the "reactionary" redefines his past and himself in terms of the infallible doctrine. Both "treatments" have meetings in which the sacred literature is studied. For the Chinese, it might be readings from "the little red book." For the AA indoctrinee, it is either the Big (blue) Book or the 12 & 12. In these study meetings, participants tell how elements of the doctrine are true and how it applies to them. If a participant doesn't think a point applies to himself, or perhaps isn't true at all, the unanimous majority helps by pointing out the "reactionary" or "alcoholic" thinking. Other Chinese meetings are for self-criticism and for expounding on their own devils, capitalism and reactionary forces, as the source of all evil. AA meetings combine the two. One may hear someone confess to a character defect and, in the same sentence, attribute the shortcoming to alcoholism.

In both Chinese re-education and the AA treatment center, the world is painted as a battleground between two forces; one pure good and one pure evil. The ultimate good for the Chinese communists is the Party, the doctrine as interpreted by the Party and everything associated with the Party. In AA, the ultimate good is AA, the doctrine as interpreted by the elders and everything associated with AA. Where one's experiences, thoughts, desires or behavior are not aligned with the "ultimate good," they are in the service of evil.

After both re-education and treatment, the prisoner and patient are thankful for the intervention of "history" or "higher power." Gratitude is felt toward the bearers of the great wisdom which transcends ordinary human concerns. For the "new man" and the "recovering alcoholic" the goal is the same: to spread the sacred doctrine.

The Red Chinese had the benefit of political power to "help" hundreds of millions of Chinese to "understand history" in a very short time. The work of "helping" sick Americans is going much slower but there are some ominous signs on the horizon. In the chilling words of an interview in Sober Times, a newspaper for people "in recovery,"

"People who are chemically dependent and codependent have a huge obligation to society to band together [politically], because we've been there and we know what the needs are in the community... Recovering people must flex their united muscle... We have to teach kids... intervene."[241]

Chapter 14

The Plight of the Grouper

When AA members return to drinking, as they frequently do, it is usually to much worse drinking than before initial AA contact. Since the program is held as perfect, the drinker and other groupers attribute this to the particular nature of "the disease."

Often, a person quits attending meetings because he is angry over being pressured to accept a particular point, or presumed point, of doctrine. For instance, a Jewish person may be told that his prayers are no good because he doesn't pray on his knees. "God won't listen unless you show humility."*

While the statement itself may have little effect, if a member's "willfulness" becomes an object of efforts at group "help," great pressure will be brought to bear. Speakers and sharers may tell how their own refusal to pray on their knees caused them great harm. Or, a speaker may tell how his "terminal uniqueness," thinking

---

*Kitty Dukakis, who is Jewish, discussed this issue in her book. In her last treatment center she learned that *as an alcoholic* she must pray on her knees. This is an excellent example of the AA-alcoholic identity superseding the religious one.

he was different from other alcoholics, caused him to think he didn't need to pray on his knees. Proper praying posi+ion may become a frequent topic of "casual" conversation at after-meeting coffee.

Pressure also takes other forms. For example, if the Jewish man should seek direction on a particular problem, he may be asked if he has prayed about it and then be asked if he prayed on his knees. If the answer is "no," he may be met with silence and body language which suggests, "Well, that explains it."

The subject may be kept at the forefront of discussion for days or weeks until someone else's crisis becomes the focus of "help," the errant grouper sees the error of his ways or he becomes angry and decides he doesn't need AA.

If he should angrily decide he doesn't need the program, it may be only the beginning of a process in which the errant grouper learns the depth of the wisdom of AA. The grouper has adopted large chunks of AA doctrine and rejecting just one small part leaves him extremely vulnerable.

In AA, one learns that anger, sadness, loneliness, and other emotions, are the work of Devil Drink and must be repressed. Most of the methods of repression an AA member has learned can't be used without AA. For instance, if one is "in danger" of becoming angry, the "resolution" may include going to meetings, public confession, working the steps, reading the Big Book, getting counsel from one's sponsor or convincing others of the miracle of recovery in AA. The person who leaves AA can't continue to repress emotion in the same ways. He also fears he will, and is unanimously expected to, return to drinking. Upon leaving, the errant grouper is likely to notice the "symptoms" of his "disease" get worse. He experiences strong feelings of "self-pity," "resentment" and fear. There are many reasons for this but none have anything to do with any disease.

During the indoctrination process, barriers went up between the grouper and pre-AA friends. His entire social group now includes predominantly or only AA members. Upon leaving AA he is *at best* left friendless and "suffering self-pity" (extremely lonely).

In all likelihood, however, his grouper friends will, out of genuine concern and fear for him, respond in a way that sabotages his ability to remain abstinent.

The most dangerous way this is done is with sincere body language which transmits the expectation of failure while giving verbal expressions of cautious optimism. For instance, if the errant member should state that he can remain "sober" without meetings, bodies will stiffen and apprehensive eyes will express genuine fear and the expectation of failure. The accompanying verbal response may be, "As long as you have a spiritual program."

Of course the errant grouper knows that AA is the only spiritual program for alcoholics. His self-doubt and fear increase.

Grouper friends may also confess to how they had left the program and how they had the same thoughts as the errant grouper now has. They will tell of the grief and danger it caused until they returned to the program. If a grouper has no such personal experience to confess, he may, out of loving kindness, tell how someone else, preferably someone who died, did exactly what the errant grouper is now doing.

The errant grouper's "disease symptoms" grow worse.

The errant AA member is locked into an identity as an alcoholic. His "disease" has long since been proven to him. He will find it extremely difficult to imagine that he could be anything but a "drinking alcoholic" or "in recovery." Unable to even imagine that there are other possibilities or even that he may not be an alcoholic, he is trapped.

AA worked to shatter his ego, allowing ego support only through belief in AA doctrine. When he leaves AA, he can no longer speak as someone who has special knowledge of God's Will. He is no longer part of the great moral crusade. He no longer has special wisdom to share. He is unable to tell others how he has found a solution to their problems.

When he leaves AA, the ex-grouper is left with his frightened, disoriented, discounted, sad, betrayed, disease-defined self and an extremely shaky ego at war with his "disease." His only remaining ego support is his abstinence.

The presence of strong emotion and the unanimous responses of his grouper friends are not the only evidence to the errant AA member that he will return to self-destructive drinking. Other evidence comes from society at large where people, influenced by 50 years of propaganda, encourage him to return to AA thinking his distress (and, in a sense, accurately so) is because he stopped attending meetings. He shouldn't be angry with AA; they are only trying to help.

With even non-grouper friends, acquaintances and authorities suggesting, "You should go back to the meetings," the errant grouper is caught in a bind. He can either return to meetings and humbly acknowledge his "willfulness" or he can decide "the whole world is wrong and I am right." The latter thought he recognizes as a disease symptom.

At this point of extreme pressure, the errant grouper often begins drinking or commits suicide. Knowing he is "powerless over alcohol," he may decide to delay his "inevitable" return to AA in the only way he knows how. Drinking will remove the intolerable "symptoms"; at least for a while.

Once he takes the first sip, all his Time, his sole remaining ego support, is gone. He can no longer say,

"Well, at least I'm sober." He is living proof of AA doctrine.

At this point, the errant grouper may have so little sense of self that he returns in terror to AA with proper penitence or proceeds to turn his anger towards himself and drinks himself to death. If his efforts to maintain "spiritual principles" and stay "sane," as defined for him in AA, are particularly successful, he may manage to be "not angry." This often ends in schizoid breaks and suicide. All of these prove to his grouper acquaintances the power of the cunning, baffling and powerful disease and the wisdom of AA.

However, the errant AA member may find he doesn't want to or even like to drink. This is not surprising since most people first go to AA because they don't want to drink any more and only went because they were told they needed to in order to stop. He may decide, "I am not an alcoholic."

Under such circumstances, his AA belief system remains intact except for the one point of doctrine which he is angry about. With a basic belief that he is helpless, inadequate and in danger of being overwhelmed by evil forces, he is extremely vulnerable to, and may even seek, another cult or cult-like group. Any similar group which understands his basic "badness" or "sickness" may be acceptable. The easiest and most frequent transition is to other Twelve Step groups. Codependents Anonymous is probably the most often chosen.

An AA member may question and become angry at some of his peers or elders over the interpretation of a particular point of doctrine. It would be extremely unusual for him, however, to question the "spiritual principles" themselves. By joining a similar group, he is merely exchanging social groups to one which won't pressure him, at least for the moment, on the particular point on which he takes a stand.

Most groupers return to excessive drinking without being overtly angry with AA. The most outstanding characteristic of these people is their intensely held belief in the goodness of AA and the badness of their self. Having unquestioned belief in the doctrine and knowing they are "powerless," they can't conceive of, and don't even try, moderating or stopping until they are ready to return to meetings.

Their explanations for drinking, while perhaps paying lip service to some event, center on the evil self as responsible. Since no one is as emotionally and intellectually dead as the doctrinal ideal, the errant grouper need only pick and choose which "manifestations of self" are most responsible.

Many of these people are actually extremely angry at AA elders, peers or doctrine. However, they "know" their anger is wrong. The Big Book stresses "resentment is the number one offender"; the number one symptom. Perhaps most convincing is the obvious sincerity and unanimity of the other groupers. A grouper has difficulty grasping the possibility that people who act out of sincere loving concern can be wrong. The fault must be within himself. Feelings of anger are repressed.

Verbal assault on the doctrine is met with extreme anger. Verbal assault on the errant grouper from the context of the doctrine is accepted as true and perhaps even greatfully acknowledged. Telling someone "the truth" is a sign of the great love in AA. Telling someone, "Maybe you have good reason to be angry" is an obvious sign of spiritual ignorance. It is dismissed out of hand.

The errant grouper may drink himself to death but since excessive drinking is its own punishment, he will probably reach a point where he wants to stop. Being thoroughly indoctrinated, he "knows" he must return to AA.

Upon his return, if the other groupers know he has

been drinking, he must show proper humility and penitence. He may, if no one knows he has been drinking, decline to confess until he has reacquired 30 days of Time with which, in most meetings, he can confess and immediately resume his status as elder authority with the newcomers.

Many people go back and forth between abstinent meeting attendance and being "out there." When a grouper is not attending meetings, he is drinking. When a grouper is attending meetings, he is not drinking. This is proof to all concerned that the program "really works."

The more often a grouper relapses, the more skillfully he adopts the repentant sinner role and the more "personal experience" he has to share about his own "sickness," the wiles of "the disease" and the wisdom of AA.

During indoctrination, words and slogans are given highly charged emotional associations. This is partly due to the unanimous emotional responses and body language of the other groupers to the language.

Another, more important way words and slogans acquire strong emotional associations is during the Fourth and Fifth step redefinition of the self. Everything which has meaning, all experience, thought and emotion, is redefined in terms of the loaded AA language. AA language elicits emotion. Emotion elicits AA language.

Information contradictory to the doctrine no longer registers properly. For example, if a family member points out to a grouper, *who never had a real drinking problem*, that he never was really an alcoholic, the grouper can not seriously consider the possibility. The family member is a "normie" and "doesn't understand" or, if he is a drinker or an alcoholic, abstinent or not, it is his "disease speaking." If he himself should think he may not be an alcoholic it is, *by definition*, a disease symptom. The thought is a dangerous one and evokes fear. Feeling fear, another trick of Devil Drink, means he is varying too far from the "spiritual." To be safe he must not think the thought. It can only lead back to the bottle.

The loaded language has many words with twisted and blurred meanings that carry strong emotional associations entirely different from normal usage. The word "sober," for example, is commonly associated with moderation and when used in reference to alcohol can also mean "not drunk." To the grouper, however, "sober" means absolutely abstinent and in AA because AAs believe those who "don't have a spiritual program" are on a "dry drunk" and do not have "emotional sobriety."

When an AA member asks another person if he is "sober," he is not asking if he is feeling the effects of intoxication. He is asking if he is maintaining absolute abstinence and perhaps if he is free of strong emotion.

A person who leaves AA, even if he remains abstinent, can not claim "true sobriety." In time, he may recover from the crisis of leaving and be happier, calmer, better adjusted and abstinent but he can not measure up to the doctrinal standards of "sobriety."

Just hearing the loaded language can cause an errant grouper to drink to excess or return to AA. What sometimes happens can perhaps best be described as "switching" or "flipping over" into the cult personality.* It is like becoming trapped in a maze. In this maze, there are many ways in (words, thoughts and feelings) but few ways out. Once within this "other personality," thought and emotion stopping techniques are "automatically" evoked.

There are many things one can do to ensure success at

---

*Steve Hassan discusses this in detail in relation to the Moonies and their language in his book "Combatting Cult Mind Control."

leaving AA. Perhaps the easiest and most immediately important is to break the closed loops making up the language by practicing new associations. In other words, rather than allowing a word or slogan to continue evoking AA associations, one can practice other, more customary associations until they become automatic and the language loses its power.

For example, the phrase "in recovery" in common usage implies "getting well." However, AA usage implies a lifetime commitment to AA. "In recovery," as AA uses it, means *staying sick forever*. "In recovery" means in a cult. The word "program" refers to something suitable for a machine, perhaps a computer or a *robot*, not a human being.

Other words can be dealt with differently. When a grouper asks, "Are you sober?," one can respond, "Are you speaking English and asking me if I am intoxicated at the moment or are you speaking Programese and asking me if I am practicing abstinence?" If the reference is to "emotional sobriety," one can be prepared to point out the more unbalanced members of AA, particularly ones with a great deal of Time. It can then be pointed out that "sobriety" as was used is peculiar to AA and a cult term.

Feeling resentment, which in common usage is not fatal, can be replaced by more common and appropriate words like irritation, anger and rage.

Love, in common usage, carries strong emotional associations. The word is extremely difficult for ex-groupers to redefine, since there is no clear English definition which covers the feelings of warmth, affection and desire, acts done out of love and the results of those acts. In AA, "love" is often the motivation for actions destructive to oneself and others. "I love myself enough to force myself to go to meetings." "We love you enough to tell you the truth. You're the cream of the crap, that's what you are." A direct parallel is the Middle Ages man

223

who took his sick wife to a physician to be bled. Did he love his wife? Of course, but it doesn't mean he wasn't killing her.

The uses and meanings of this word can become more sharply focused and removed from the cult context by substituting the less ambitious word "respect." Am I *respecting* myself? Are they *respecting* me? Am I *respecting* them?

Perhaps the word which is most difficult to redefine, and which has the widest range of definitions and associations in common usage, is "spiritual." One definition which most helped me was "that which gives feelings of worth, belonging and connectedness." While I have found no organization which is *perfect* on all three counts, by this definition, AA is grossly unspiritual on all counts. AA teaches that the self is worthless and gives "belonging" (as a "diseased" person) at the cost of connectedness with the human race (we alcoholics and you normies). Even in their own terms of humility, isn't it *arrogant* for Twelve-Step members to assume that they and they alone are sane and purely spiritual and everyone else is insane and needs their "spiritual" help?

The clichés also need new associations. Since most are exclusive to AA and would never be used in ordinary conversation, all that is necessary for most of them is to come up with a few associations which show their logical flaws. Making fun of them is particularly appropriate because ridicule is the exact opposite of the reverence in which they are held. It saps their power. For example, one might try thinking, "Alcoholics rarely recover on their own, unless, of course, they are shipwrecked alone on a desert island." Or, "Alcoholics rarely recover on their own; alcoholics never recover in AA." (According to AA doctrine one is always "recovering," never recovered.) Also, "No one ever drank while working the steps, but they usually drink a lot more afterwards."

This is not to suggest that one should ridicule the groupers. The point is, *especially* in one's own mind, to neutralize the power of the language. It is also important to protect oneself from interacting with groupers in a way which creates confusion and leaves oneself open to suggestion.

Language and identity mix in the words "I am an alcoholic." In all Twelve-Step groups, members adopt a "disease" as the central core of their identity. This identity can be exchanged for broader, more accurate, self-definitions. First and foremost, most general and inarguable, one can say "I am a human being." While this may seem obvious, for the grouper it is a radical concept. Beyond that, one may *partially* identify oneself in an almost infinite number of ways including by profession, relationships with other people, politically, socially, religiously, and by interests and hobbies. People are not their "disease."

Chapter 15

Moderation and Abstention

There is some evidence that abstinence is an easier goal for most older, married persons and that moderation is easier for most younger, single people. But, what *may be* easier is just one factor and not by itself grounds for a decision. There is no authority, other than a physician pointing to specific disease conditions such as diabetes and liver problems, who can tell someone else whether they must abstain altogether rather than moderate. Someone who belongs to a church which uses wine in Communion services won't want to, and doesn't need to be, *absolutely* abstinent. Other than the exigencies of health and religion, the most critical factor in choosing a goal is what a person *believes* he can do and what he *wants* to do.

Beginning moderate drinking after long-term abstinence has many pitfalls and is not recommended. The only serious problem with abstinence as a goal is its difficulty for most people. If someone is already successful, why tamper with success? An advantage of the goal of moderation is that the option is always open to abstain if it is later decided to be *easier*, which for some people it is. Perhaps the best way to begin moderation, however, is by abstaining for two weeks or so. The benefits are two-fold.

First, tolerance decreases and a relatively small amount of alcohol will give an appreciably greater effect. Second, by paying careful attention to oneself, to the feelings and thoughts that arise while abstaining, the role of the excessive drinking comes more clearly into focus.

For example, a person who feels extremely lonely when he abstains will be able to focus his attention on finding better ways of interacting with others. If he feels helpless or powerless, he can look for ways to regain the perception of control in his life.

It is important that a person who has been drinking to great excess see a physician. Medical advice can be helpful and perhaps even life-saving but any suggestion by one's doctor that "people rarely recover on their own," that one should go to AA or that one should meet someone "in recovery" can be ignored. It is also important to take note of the doctor's body language and, if it is discouraging of one's decision to quit or moderate without "help," to consciously discount the source.*

Although strong emotion may be experienced, abstaining or moderating is not necessarily difficult. While it may seem overwhelming for some who decide to "never drink again," it is relatively easy to ignore "forever" and merely postpone or delay a decision to drink; to just do something else.

---

*Many physicians just don't know. Traditionally, they have had little education about problem drinking since it wasn't considered a disease until fairly recently. Now that it has been voted a disease, their "education" about drinking problems originates with members of the medical profession who are also AA members. If you have, or wish to have, a long-standing relationship with your doctor, you may want to loan him this book. It is helpful to have a supportive physician rather than one *who is trying to be supportive by suggesting failure.*

For example, someone in the habit of drinking after work, instead of worrying about the difficulty of, or struggle in, abstaining forever, will find it far easier to just go to a movie, watch TV, meet friends for dinner, go on a date or read a book.

Central to maintaining moderation or abstinence is having or developing a "can do" belief and motivation. Motivation can perhaps be best thought of in terms of what you "would rather" do. Humans are rarely clear-cut in their motivation. For example, someone who is planning a vacation may want to go to two mutually exclusive places. Perhaps he wants to go to Europe and to South America but only has two weeks off work and a limited budget. He *wants to* go to both. What he actually does in based on what he "would rather" do.

The same is true when choosing whether or how much to drink on any given occasion. Mixed emotion often plays a part. Wanting to drink is not a sign of looming failure. Comfortable success in abstention or moderation doesn't necessarily depend on feeling horror or revulsion at the thought of drinking but on the development of "would rathers." For example, someone who has decided to abstain may have an urge to go out on Saturday night for a few drinks at his old hangout. This is no "big deal" and need not lead to "relapse" or failure. All he needs is to find one thing he would *rather* do. Then he not only doesn't drink, he doesn't feel cheated.

Important for the abstainer, when "craving" (wanting) a drink, is to have alternative ways to *better* meet the same ends. Someone who has been abstinent for several months may find himself looking forward to the day he can "control" his drinking. Of course, people can and do control their drinking when they want to but they are less likely to want to as long as they remain blind to the reasons they drink and can't see better ways of filling their needs. The most important point is to not waste time pining for what is not available but to recognize and take full advantage of present opportunities. By finding better ways to accomplish what one did in the past by drinking, the desire to drink progressively diminishes.

Taking accurate notice of the costs and benefits of excessive drinking helps develop motivation. For example, a man who is angry with his wife may gain a sense of control in his life by storming out and getting drunk. He is "in control." She isn't. While a sense of control of one's life is essential to well-being, by recognizing and carefully weighing all alternatives, better choices can be found which give the perception of control without doing harm and perhaps are even constructive. He may decide he would rather honestly discuss the underlying problem with his wife, work out a compromise, go for relationship counseling or get a divorce. By being aware of, and carefully considering, all possible alternatives, one can find something one would *rather* do than drink.

The person who drinks as a substitute for real intimacy can work on intimacy problems and, though he may *want* to drink, he may find that he'd not only *rather* share real intimacy, but that he is more than competent and capable of doing so.

Developing motivation and a sense of competence and capability are mutually supportive. The more one wants to quit or moderate, the easier it is to do so. Realizing that one would rather not drink powerfully counteracts lessons of learned helplessness concerning drinking. The more obtainable the goal of stopping or moderating seems, the less grief expected in reaching the goal, the more desirable a course of action it becomes.

Essential to developing a sense of competence is to think in terms of *how* one will succeed instead of *how* one will fail. "Slips" or "relapses," should they occur, can be thought of as failure *but they can't occur without success.* They can also be great learning opportunities. One can ask oneself "Why did I?", "What did I expect to be the advantage?", "Was there a 'pay-off'?", "What are the disadvantages?" and, most importantly, "What better choices are there and how will I make them next time?"

Drinking more or behaving worse when drinking upon deciding to quit or moderate can be good signs. *The higher the price paid for drinking to excess, the more difficult it is to continue.*

Abstaining for two weeks to decrease tolerance is helpful because it enhances the pleasurable effects of alcohol.

It might seem odd to suggest that someone with a drinking problem should work to enhance the drinking experience. However, excessive drinking is heavily based on false expectations. The more clearly a problem drinker discriminates between when drinking is pleasurable and productive and when it is unpleasant and destructive, the more difficult it is to continue excessive drinking.

Two entirely different drinking styles point out the benefits of drinking for maximum pleasurable effect. Imagine a man who, on an empty stomach, slowly sips two drinks and feels pleasantly "high" for a couple of hours. During that time, he may enjoy stimulating conversation and music. If he is having a good time, he may stay a little longer. If he is not enjoying himself, he'll leave sooner. After drinking, he eats and quickly becomes unintoxicated. The next morning he wakes up sharp and alert, ready to take advantage of the day.

In contrast with this "social drinker," imagine a man who customarily drinks large quantities of alcohol. Due to his steady high consumption, he needs to drink a lot to feel a little effect. When he drinks on a full stomach, he needs to drink even more. In the morning he is groggy and hung-over so he guzzles hugh amounts of coffee. This creates a need to drink even more when he does drink to feel an effect. While he may have some pleasant experiences while drinking, he stays "high" long after the pleasure is gone and will continue drinking whether he is enjoying the experience or not. He also disrupts his ability to sleep well. He suffers hangovers and the long-term health consequences of excessive drinking.

It is important for the moderator to carefully discriminate between a desire to drink for a pleasant experience and drinking to avoid undesired feelings and ignore problems. Before drinking, one can ask, "Do I feel good?" and "Do I have unpleasant feelings I want to drown out?" If the answer to the latter is yes, drinking is never in one's best interest. If the goal is abstention, the question to ask when feeling good is, "Do I want to risk changing it?"

While drinking, it is important for the moderator to notice whether he is enjoying himself and whether the environment is pleasantly stimulating. When it is not, it helps to develop the habit of stopping drinking and doing something else. For some people, since so much of drinking behavior is merely the habit of sipping or gulping, it is helpful to have a glass of water or soft drink to sip on. It also helps to do "intoxication checks"; to frequently take careful notice of the physical and mental effects of drinking. It is rather pointless to drink for the "high" and not pay attention to one's body, to ignore the effects. The more attuned one is to the effects, the less one needs to drink to feel them.

Paying close attention to emotional states and their effect on drinking helps. If an angry or sad thought comes to mind, what is its effect on drinking behavior? Do you reach for the glass? Do you take bigger gulps? Just noticing the behavior and the futility of it can help maintain moderation.

Closely related is taking notice of the environment. Drinking in an unpleasant environment is likely to be an unpleasant experience. Drinking in a pleasant environment is likely to be pleasurable. Much of the enjoyment in drinking comes, not from the alcohol itself, but from the environment and one's own mood and expectations.

Of course, if someone clearly would rather get very drunk or clearly would rather drink moderately, not much will make a difference.* However, people are often somewhere between the two and any little substitute habit, awareness or effort can have dramatic effects.

When drinking more and enjoying it less, it is important to ask oneself what one would *really* rather do; what would be more fulfilling. There is no real benefit to alcohol except as a mild social lubricant. It fills no real needs.

In studying drinkers whose goal was abstention, it was found that those who succeeded felt confident and capable and had "multiple ways of dealing with stress." Those who "relapsed" drank over frustration, anger, social pressure and interpersonal conflict.[242] In other words, those who returned to self-destructive drinking did so in response to more-or-less everyday stress. Those who succeeded had multiple ways of responding in stressful situations.

The stresses leading to excessive drinking are chronic although perhaps intermittent. To a large degree, the responses to those stresses are subconscious and automatic. The dynamics of a particular situation may be entirely out of the conscious awareness of the problem drinker. He may be mystified by his drinking.

There is no single way to deal with stress nor is stress itself the problem. For example, imagine a man in a

---

*For someone to recognize that he would rather drink excessively, even if he then does so, can be a good start in getting a handle on the problem.

forest being chased by a pack of wolves. It certainly is a stressful situation. What does he do to deal with the stress? Does he meditate, exercise or take relaxation therapy? Or does he deal with the *problem* and climb a tree?

Parallel situations exist in everyday life. Someone who has an unsuitable job becomes "stressed out." There are many things he can do to deal with the stress, to make the undesired feelings go away, including drinking or meditating. That takes care of the stress. It doesn't, however, solve the problem. He still has unsuitable work.

Someone may feel "stressed out" over an intolerable relationship. The stress can be "dealt with." It can be made to go away. He still, however, has a bad relationship.

The problem drinker who is having continued trouble moderating or abstaining needs a greater awareness of his problems, of his choices for solving them and of his power to make those choices. The tools for this greater awareness lie within the problem drinker's much-scorned and disparaged self.[*]

---

[*]See Appendix D for further reading about the self.

Afterword

Recovery from Self-Betrayal
by Alice Miller

Throughout time, people in distress have been seeking help from others: from sages, priests, gurus, psychologists and groups of different kinds. They have never known that, for the most part, out of all these people, none could lend real assistance because they too, like most other human beings, fear the only truth that can really help. That truth is about the origins of human suffering: the repressed tragic experiences of our childhood. **The repression of injuries endured in childhood is the hidden cause of our later suffering.**

For the child, this repression was necessary because otherwise he would have died from the overwhelming pain. However, adults need not die if they decide to become conscious. They can set themselves free from their symptoms and, at long last, be happy in themselves and in their lives as soon as they acknowledge the old wounds and let them heal. This becomes possible when we feel the strong emotions we had to repress in childhood in order to survive, when we take them seriously, clarify their meaning and learn that our pain and rage are justified. This happens when we condemn the abuse without so-called moral objections and find our genuine, authentic needs. Anything else we may do, however well rooted in our culture and tradition, is betrayal and self-betrayal as long as it is based on the denial of truth and on the ignorance of real, provable knowledge.

What do we do if suddenly we hear unusual noises in our car? Or if we even suspect it is not running well? We take it to a skilled mechanic to find out what is wrong. We expect him to check the car and to find out why it is not running well before he proceeds to repair it. We would not entrust our car to a person uninterested in finding the cause of the problem or who would stubbornly dispute its importance. We would probably easily recognize that such a mechanic would make matters even worse.

But what we do for our car we are very often unable to do for ourselves. We often deliver up our souls without hesitation to exactly this kind of "expert." Why? Why are we able to take account of the skill of a person before we entrust him with our car but not with someone we decide to entrust with our soul? Is it because we learned from our parents early in our lives to ignore the existence of our soul: its laws, its plight, its despair and its needs? Is it because we learned to not care, to not feel the endured humiliations, to not know our rights, and to not ask questions? Is it because we are unaware of our own life history and don't want to know it for we are too afraid of feeling old pain? Or is it simply because we do not know how to feel this pain or that we can feel it safely? All these reasons, together, probably give the explanation. People abused and betrayed in childhood, and there are few who were not at the very least betrayed by "poisonous pedagogy" (cf. A.M., "For Your Own Good," FSG, 1983), are not free to see through manipulation unless they lose their blindness in an effective therapy; they accept absurdities without resistance because that is what they are used to. Until recently, nobody actually knew how we could bring our forgotten (but stored up in our body and still very active) life history to light and, in this light, alleviate our pain. This concept has nothing to do with Freud and his followers. It is a new discovery, not yet taught in universities.

What would we do if we were hit by a reckless driver and left with a broken leg? We would have a doctor treat the injury as soon as possible so that it could heal properly. We would not go to a priest who would ask us to pray, or to an exorcist to cast out demons. Nor would we go to other people with broken bones who would treat our predicament as bad behavior and advise us how to behave, who would lead us to believe that everything would be OK if only we manage to forget the pain and the broken bones and forgive the driver. At least where our bones are concerned, we would regard such demands as unreasonable and bizarre.

But again, not if it is a question of our soul. When our heart and our soul are broken we often go to ignorant and blind people who may even go so far as to ridicule our invisible but very real fracture. We go to people who can not or do not want to understand because they are so terribly frightened of their own pain, pain over which they fear being misunderstood or ridiculed. They sometimes call themselves therapists but don't realize they are only trying to escape from their own painful history, to "cure" themselves at our cost. They treat us according to the principles they themselves learned from their own childhood treatment: "You must behave and remain lifeless, exactly as I was forced to do, you too must give up your feelings, your truth." We also go to people who pretend to be the highest authority in "recovery" today, but who use, uncritically, the poisonous pedagogy: "We understand your anger with the driver, we even encourage you to feel it, but only for a while. Then you have to pull yourself together, let your feelings go, exercise 'detachment' and 'positive thinking' and, above all, you must forgive or else your bones will never heal." "Why not?", we should be able to ask, "Isn't the recovery process dependent on the truth of the feelings and needs stored in our body? Don't our feelings and needs reveal important messages? Why do you want to take them away from us? Don't you realize how destructive your so-called 'moral' chatter is?"

Even though this "morality" is well-rooted in our traditions and religions, killing one's feelings is contrary to Nature. Animals kill their young if they are sick and too weak to survive, but the healthy ones enjoy care and protection so they can live. Only the human child is condemned to an existence between life and death. It is no wonder so many people, looking for a means to escape this horror, end up addicted: to alcohol, to drugs, to overeating or to attending daily group meetings. But an addiction is not a safe refuge and, above all, it is no longer necessary. A different, healthy way to get rid of the horror has been found: to face it, to feel it, and to resolve its consequences. Even for those who have always tried to escape from their wounds because this seemed to be the one and only healthy way out, today, for the first time in our history, there is another option. We can make a choice. We can save our lives when we are prepared to search out our truth and when we refuse to be intimidated by the ridicule and ignorance of others. Now there is a method that enables us to access our life history, not with hypnosis, but by giving us complete leadership, autonomy and responsibility. This method has been very carefully developed by the Swiss therapist J. Konrad Stettbacher and is set out in detail in his book, "Making Sense of Suffering" (Dutton, 1991). It has been tested by many people, myself included. Since the first

German publication in 1990, which has been followed by seven further reprints, we have learned that people can succeed, with the help of this description, to start their journey into their past, to discover their real biography and to alleviate even the most serious symptoms. Next year a collection of Stettbacher's answers to readers working with his therapy will appear under the title: "Responses to Questions out of Hell."

I think I owe this information to all those people who have written to me and who not only reject addiction as a way of dealing with problems and feared emotions but who also reject obedience as a way of adult life; for people who want to come in touch with their feelings and their truth, even if doing this work still frightens them; for people who are longing for a full life and do not know they have a right to it; for people who want to find their memories, memories locked up in frozen feelings, but who are unaware of the path leading to them. They are abstinent but suffer from depression or other forms of confusion and self-betrayal in spite of ten years or longer in various programs. The way they use my information does not depend on me, but, for the most part, on their own life history. Once they start to explore this very history, they will escape from their plight and discover new options they never before could have imagined existed.

Dear Reader, when you read that I am recommending Stettbacher's method to heal, you should not follow blindly. You should check what I am saying on your own. You are free to discover if this therapy works for you or not. In any case, you do not have to believe in the "higher power" to make it work. The "higher power" will not do anything for you if you refuse to obey and refuse to remain blind. You have to do the work on your own with the help of Stettbacher's explanation. And you can do it because what you are going to find has always been within you. It has given you considerable anguish but only because it was denied, avoided and feared. Once you can face it, it will help you, it will guide you. You will recognize your fear as what it really is. Perhaps it is simply the fear of the child who is afraid of punishment if he acknowledges and speaks the truth. But you will not be punished now. **Now, as an adult, you can insist on your right to feel your reality.** You no longer need to cling to the empty word "spirituality," a word that is meaningless because it is used for everything and says nothing that can't be said without using it. Your **real, felt** feelings will never kill you; they will help you find direction. Only the unfelt yet powerful emotions and needs, the feared and banished ones, can kill us. Researchers are now beginning to grasp the truth that cancer can often be the last available, the ultimate, language of these repressed feelings. Therapists were surprised to see that once patients could feel, could express themselves, could take their unwanted emotions seriously and develop them into a direct and healthy language, full recovery was possible. (Cf. Linda Temoshock and Henry Dreher, The Type C Connection, Random House, 1992).

To properly heal a broken bone you must consult a doctor. But **the specific causes of your suffering can only be found by yourself.** With the right instruction you can find them. When you are on the path toward your unique, unmistakable life history, you are mending your "fractures." Only one person can fully understand and heal them: you. The better you learn to take your feelings seriously and to understand them in depth with Stettbacher's technique, the quicker you will see through lies, humiliations and manipulations, and the more strongly you will be able to resist them.

Alcoholism, as well as any other addiction, will disappear during this inner quest. What is addiction really? It is a sign, a signal, a symptom of distress. It is a language that tells us about a plight that **must not be understood**. The drug business would not flourish if there were not so many people who, in refusing to acknowledge their wounds, are in a permanent state of self-betrayal. Thus, people work to get rid of symptoms instead of searching out the cause.

There are plenty of means to combat symptoms: medication, sermons, numerous "treatments," "miracles," threats, cults, pedagogical indoctrination and even blackmail. They can all work for a while, but only because they reinforce the repression and reinforce the fear of resolving it. However, many people who become abstinent this way are driven into another addiction because the real reasons for becoming addicted must be kept hidden. A lot of money and fame comes from this business of repression because it satisfies the longings of so many grown-up children: **to be loved as a good child** (I am as blind as you want me to be. I am ready to forget all your cruelty, even at the cost of my life. Can you love me now?). In the long term, we have to pay a high price for this repression. The repressed story continues to try, again and again, to at long last be heard. Thus, your plight will look for other symptoms, another language, until it is taken seriously enough. Alcoholism, just one of many forms of addiction, is an attempt by a person in despair, **who is not allowed to be in despair,** to drown his memory and his plight in alcohol, to get rid of his memory, to forget his plight. Of course, this "solution" is no longer needed if the goal is exactly the opposite, if you **want** to remember, if you want to feel your plight and to understand its reasons, if you slowly become aware of **why** you were so afraid of acknowledging the reasons. This can happen once you decide to stop running away, to stop betraying yourself, to allow the truth to enter your consciousness. You decide to do so because you finally understand that everything else is useless and because you no longer want to watch your life go by before having even begun to live. You decide to stop betraying yourself because you understand that only you can give yourself the love and care you never received and that you can't do that as long as you deny the truth.

My recommendation of Stettbacher's therapy cannot be extended to any other I am familiar with. Unfortunately, therapists who are trained in this technique are still rare. If you feel that you need the help of somebody in becoming familiar with Stettbacher's method, or of someone simply as an "enlightened witness" (Cf. AM, "Banished Knowledge," Doubleday, 1990), you can look for a therapist who himself honestly tries to clear up his or her feelings and needs with the help of this method. If a person who calls himself a therapist tells you he doesn't need it, if he is not willing to thoroughly read "Making Sense of Suffering" and to work on it, but instead expresses general judgements; if he is obviously unable to discuss your questions concerning this therapy with you in detail, he will not be of any help to you. Sooner or later he will confuse you because of his own opposition and fears and he will impede the process of your liberation.

In any case, don't try to resolve the fears of your "helpers." If others refuse to do their work on their own, you can not do it for them. No one can do it for anyone except for oneself. But you can refuse to pay the bill for their fears. You can refuse to let them use you to maintain their blindness. The more familiar you become with your biography, the better you will have learned to perceive your internal signals and take them seriously, and the easier you can judge whether people who call themselves therapists follow along with you and help you or whether they only serve to confuse you more. If you don't want to pay the bill for someone else's confusion, you must have the strength and the wisdom to give up a therapist as you would give up a mechanic who politely but blindly tried to fix your car while ignoring and wanting to ignore what was really wrong in the first place. He may be a nice person but as long as he can damage you, your life may be in danger. It is, then, your life that must have priority and nothing else.

Appendix A

The Liberating Experience of Painful Truth

by Alice Miller

THE MISTREATED AND NEGLECTED CHILD IS
completely alone in the darkness of confusion and fear.
Surrounded by arrogance and hatred, robbed of its rights
and its speech, deceived in its love and its trust, disre-
garded, humiliated, mocked in its pain, such a child is
blind, lost, and pitilessly exposed to the power of ignorant
adults. It is without orientation and completely defense-
less.

Its whole being would like to shout out its anger, give
voice to its feeling of outrage, call for help. But that is
exactly what it may not do. All its normal reactions, the
reactions with which nature has endowed it to help it
survive, remain blocked. If no witness comes to its aid,
these natural reactions would enlarge and prolong the
child's sufferings. Ultimately, the child could die of them.

Thus, the healthy impulse to protest against inhuman-
ity has to be suppressed. The child attempts to extin-
guish and erase from memory everything that has
happened to it, in order to banish from consciousness the

burning outrage, fury, fear, and the unbearable pain — as it hopes, forever. What remains is a feeling of its own guilt, rather than outrage that it is forced to kiss the hand that beat it and beg for forgiveness — something that unfortunately happens more than one imagines.

The abused child goes on living within those who have survived such torture, a torture that ended with total *repression*. *They* live with the darkness of fear, oppression, and threats. When all its attempts to move the adult to heed its story have failed, it resorts to the language of symptoms to make itself heard. Enter addiction, psychosis, criminality.

If, as adults, we nevertheless begin to have an inkling of why we are suffering and ask a specialist whether these sufferings could have a connection with our childhood, we will usually be told that this is very unlikely to be the case. And if it were, that we should learn forgiveness. It is the resentment at the past, we are told, that is making us ill.

In those by-now familiar groups in which addicts and their relations go into therapy together, the following belief is invariably expressed. Only when you have forgiven your parents for everything they did to you can you get well. Even if both your parents were alcoholics, even if they mistreated, confused, exploited, beat, and totally overloaded you, you must forgive them everything. Otherwise, your illness will not be cured. There are many programs going by the name of "therapy," whose basis consists of first learning to express one's feelings in order to see what happened in childhood. Then, however, comes "the work of forgiveness," which is apparently necessary if one is to heal. Many young people who have AIDS or are drug-addicted die in the wake of their effort to forgive so much. What they do not realize is that they are dying in order to keep the repression of their childhood intact.

The majority of therapists fear this truth. They work under the influence of destructive interpretations culled from both Western and Oriental religions, which preach forgiveness to the once-mistreated child. Thereby, they create a new vicious circle for people who, from their earliest years, have been caught in the vicious circle of pedagogy. This, they refer to as "therapy." In so doing, they lead them into a trap from which there is no escape, the same trap that once rendered their natural protests impossible, thus causing the illness in the first place. Because such therapists, caught as they are in the pedagogic system, cannot help patients to resolve the consequences of the traumatization they have suffered, they offer them traditional morality instead.

In recent years I have been sent many books from the United States of America describing different kinds of therapeutic intervention by authors with whom I am not familiar. Without a single exception, all these authors presume that forgiveness is a condition for a "successful" therapy. This notion appears to be so widespread in therapeutic circles that it is never called into question – something urgently needed. For forgiveness does not resolve latent hatred and self-hatred but rather covers them up in a very dangerous way.

I know of the case of one woman, whose mother was sexually abused as a child by both her father and brother. Reared in a convent, this woman learned "the blessing of forgiveness" by heart. She continued to worship her father and brother without the slightest trace of bitterness. While her daughter was still an infant, she frequently left the child "in the care of" her thirteen-year-old nephew, while she went blithely off to the movies with her husband. While she was gone, the pubescent babysitter indulged his sexual desires on the body of her baby daughter. When the daughter later sought help in psychoanalytic counseling, the analyst told her she should on no account blame her mother. Her intentions had not been bad, she was told. She had had no idea that her babysitter was routinely abusing her child. The mother, it seems, was literally clueless. When the child began to develop dietary disturbances, she anxiously consulted a number of doctors. They assured her that the disturbances in her eating habits came from "teething." Thus, the gears of this forgiveness-machine were functioning almost perfectly – and, at the expense of the truth and the lives of all concerned.

In her book *The Obsidian Mirror* (Seattle, 1988), Louise Wisechild describes how she succeeded in deciphering her body's messages and communications, and thereby her feelings, so that she was gradually able to free her childhood from repression. This took place during her training as a massage-therapist and involved body-work and written accounts of her experiences. Gradually, she discovered in detail events that she had totally banished from consciousness: that she had been sexually molested by her grandfather at the age of four; that she was subsequently grossly abused by a perverted uncle; and that she was finally raped by her step-father. As the pattern of self-destructiveness was not resolved simply by this knowledge, she went to a woman therapist who was willing to work with her further on this horrific journey of self-discovery. Disregarding the manifest torture to which the patient had been subjected, the therapist told her one day, "If you don't forgive your mother, you will never be able to forgive yourself." Instead of helping the patient to resolve the guilt feelings that had been imposed upon her – the ultimate purpose, presumably, of therapy – she was burdened with an additional demand, a demand that could only serve to cement those feelings of guilt. A quasi-religious act of forgiveness can never resolve patterns of self-destruction.

Why should this woman, after showing her concern for

her mother for thirty years, forgive her crime, when that mother had never made the slightest effort to see what she had done to her daughter? On one occasion, as the child, rigid with fear and disgust, was forced to lie under the heavy, male body of her uncle, she caught sight of her mother in the mirror as she approached the door. The child hoped to be saved, but the mother turned and disappeared. When Louise was an adult, she heard her mother say that she could only cope with her fear of that uncle if her children were around her. When the daughter tried to discuss her rape at the hands of her stepfather, her mother wrote her that she never wished to see her again. To me, it is incredible that even in such a blatant case the pressure to forgive, which effectively prevents the chance of a successful therapy, is not shown up for the absurd demand that it is. It is just this pressure to forgive that mobilizes old fears in the patient that oblige him or her to believe such an authority. What can it possibly achieve, except a quiet conscience for the therapist?

This example shows how much can be destroyed with a single, fundamentally wrong, confusing sentence. That it is well anchored in tradition and has been implanted in us since our earliest childhood only makes matters worse. What is involved here is an outrageous misuse of power, by which therapists are wont to ward off their powerlessness and fear. Patients, for their part, are convinced that the therapist holds this view as a result of the incontrovertible evidence of experience and so believe this "authority." They cannot know – and it is almost impossible for them to discover – that what this claim in fact discloses is the therapist's own fear of the mistreatment suffered at the hands of his or her parents. How are patients meant to resolve their feelings of guilt under such circumstances? On the contrary, they will simply be confirmed.

Preaching forgiveness reveals the pedagogic nature of most "therapy." In addition, it exposes the powerlessness of the preachers. In a sense, it is odd that they call themselves "therapists" at all. "Priests" would be more apt. What ultimately emerges is the continuation of the blindness inherited in childhood, the blindness that a real therapy could relieve. What is constantly repeated to patients – until they believe it, and the therapist is mollified – is: "Your hate is making you ill. You must forgive and forget. Then you will be well." But it was not hatred that drove patients to mute desperation in their childhood, by alienating them from their feelings and their needs. It was such morality with which they were constantly pressured.

In my own therapy, using the method outlined by J. Konrad Stettbacher in his book *Making Sense of Suffering* (New York, 1991), it was my experience that it was precisely the opposite of forgiveness – namely, rebellion against mistreatment suffered, the recognition and condemnation of my parents' destructive opinions and actions, and the articulation of my own needs – that ultimately freed me from the past. In my childhood, these things had been ignored in the name of "a good upbringing," and I myself learned to ignore them for decades in order to be the "good" and "tolerant" child my parents wished me to be. But today I know: I always needed to expose and fight against opinions and attitudes that I considered destructive of life wherever I encountered them, and not to tolerate them. But I could only do this effectively once I had felt and experienced what was inflicted on me earlier. By preventing me from feeling the pain, the moral-religious injunction to forgive did nothing but hinder this process.

The demand for forgiveness has nothing to do with either an effective therapy or life. For many people in search of help, it closes the path to freedom. Therapists allow themselves to be led by their own fear – the mistreated child's fear of its parents' revenge – and by the hope that good behavior might one day be able to buy the love their parents denied them. The price that patients have to pay for this illusory hope is high indeed. Given false information, they cannot find the path to self-fulfillment.

By refusing to forgive, I give up all illusions. A mistreated child, of course, cannot live without them. But a grown-up therapist must be able to manage it. His or her patients should be able to ask: "Why should I forgive, when no one is asking me to? I mean, my parents refuse to understand and to know what they did to me. So why should I go on trying to understand and forgive my parents and whatever happened in their childhood, with things like psychoanalysis and transactional analysis? What's the use? Whom does it help? It doesn't help my parents to see the truth. But it does prevent me from experiencing my feelings, the feelings that would give me access to the truth. But under the bell-jar of forgiveness, feelings cannot and may not blossom freely." Such reflections are, unfortunately, not common in therapeutic circles, in which forgiveness is the ultimate law. The only compromise that is made consists of differentiating between false and correct forms of forgiveness. But therapy requires only the "correct" form. And this goal may never be questioned.

I have asked many therapists why it is that they believe their patients must forgive if they are to become well, but I have never received a halfway acceptable answer. Clearly, they had never questioned their assertion. It was, for them, as self-evident as the mistreatment with which they grew up. I cannot conceive of a society in which children are not mistreated, but respected and lovingly cared for, that would develop an ideology of forgiveness for incomprehensible cruelties. This ideology is indivisible with the command "Thou shalt not be aware" and with the repetition of that cruelty on the next generation. It is our children who pay the price for our forgiveness of our parents. Our fear of their revenge is the basis of our morality.

Only by means of gradual therapeutic disclosure that dispenses with bogus morality and pedagogy can this calamitous ideology be stopped. Survivors of mistreatment need to discover their own truth if they are to free themselves of its consequences. The effort spent on the work of forgiveness leads them away from this truth.

An effective therapy cannot be achieved if the mechanisms of pedagogy continue to operate. It requires recognition of the damage caused by our upbringing, whose consequences it can resolve. It must make patients' feelings available to them – and this for the entirety of their lives. Only this can help them to orientate and be at one with themselves. Moralizing appeals can only result in barring access to the truth.

A child can excuse its parents, if they in their turn are prepared to recognize and admit to their failures. But the demand for forgiveness that I constantly encounter poses a positive danger for therapy; the expression of our culture. Mistreatment of children is the order of the day and those errors are *therefore* trivialized by the majority of adults. Forgiving has negative consequences, not only for the individual, but for society at large, because it means disguising destructive opinions and attitudes, and involves drawing a curtain across reality so that we cannot see what is taking place behind it.

The possibility of change depends on whether there is a sufficient number of enlightened witnesses to create a safety net for the growing consciousness of those who have been mistreated as children, so that they do not fall into the darkness of forgetfulness, from which they will later emerge as criminals or the mentally ill. Cradled in the "net" provided by such enlightened witnesses, these children can grow to be conscious adults, adults who live *with* and not against their past and who will *therefore* be able to do everything they can to create a more humane future for us all.

There are people who are not part of the massive flight from the truth, people who resist the injunction not to look back, dare look back and refuse to let themselves be deterred in their purpose by arrogance of any kind. J. Konrad Stettbacher is one of them. The description of his therapeutic method has enabled many survivors of childhood mistreatment to confront their past. In my introduction to his book, which has now been published in English, I wrote the following:

> *The publication of this book represents an immense challenge to all existing schools of therapy. J. Konrad Stettbacher's therapy furnishes proof that it is possible to resolve childhood repression safely and without confusion – something that has always been disputed by the most respected schools of thought.*
>
> *How much unnecessary suffering would I, my children, and their future children, have been spared if I had been able to read this book when I was young and at that stage of my life been able to become fully conscious of my childhood. How many wrong turns would I have been able to spare myself and my patients if it had been available to me after my studies and before I began the misleading training to work as a psychoanalyst. but at that time Stettbacher's primal therapy did not exist. It first had to be experienced, tested, conceptualized and, finally, described. Only now is it available to the public.*
>
> *My sadness at what escaped me for so long is tempered by the fact that this book will help many others to orientate themselves before they take the*

momentous step of getting married and having children. With the help of this book, older people may also be able to find a way out of the maze that imprisons them, ways that are not destructive and will open unimaginable new horizons.

Thanks to this book, they will discover that, contrary to Freud's contention, the reality of childhood is available to us and not through artificial and potentially dangerous means like LSD, hypnosis, rebirthing, and similar forms of therapy, but slowly, step by step, with respect for our natural defense mechanisms. The book demonstrates that the injured person is in a position to reconstruct the history of his wounds and resolve them. With the help of our feelings we can discover the truth about our childhood traumas.

This is a revolutionary discovery with far-reaching consequences. With the publication of this book, it will be almost impossible to go on distracting the victims of childhood abuse from their true history with arcane theories, ambiguous symbols, meditation, or, worse, medication – unless, in certain cases, the real situation of the child was so inconceivable that the adult will have to continue to be caught in the game of conceptual blindman's buff. For those who really wish to know the truth, this book proves that this is absolutely possible.

Repression may have had a function in helping us to survive childhood horrors, but as adults it prevents us from living consciously and responsibly. Most people do not know that they were injured as children and that it is these very injuries which prevent them from valuing and caring for life. Instead, they in turn injure their own children, calling this maltreatment "toughening up," "education," or "socialization." Repression of their first experiences, which helped the child to survive, now presents the adult with a bill in the form of a binding command: *"Thou shalt not be aware."* Once we have realized that there is a way to repossess that lost consciousness to the full, we can stop paying off that account. From now on, no serious therapist will be able to ignore that discovery.

J. Konrad Stettbacher's path to a systematic resolution of repression represents a breakthrough, a fully new concept of help and self-help, without the significant pedagogy. At the same time, it offers a view on human nature , a radical new anthropology, that opens to us as yet ignored vistas. For as soon as there are enough therapists who, from their own experience, have recognized the dynamics of child abuse, we can put an end to the vicious circle of human destruction and self-destruction.

I have undergone this therapy myself and felt its astonishing, holistic effect on the body, mind and emotions. Because I have done so, I have no hesitation in recommending it to others. To be able to do this is also a great relief for me. Since the appearance of my early books more than ten years ago, I have been asked again and again to recommend therapists who work in conformity with my own findings. As my books evidently contradict almost everything which therapists still learn and practice today I was, with the best will in the world, not able to do so.

Only in this concept have I found a therapy which fully takes into account the realities of child abuse. J. K. Stettbacher is incorruptible in his judgments. He is not blinded or unnerved by fear. The theory he has evolved does not gloss over anything or veil it in secrecy. It does not preach forgiveness. Above all, it refuses to let anything deflect it form its duty as the attorney of the injured child. The contrast to traditional views, attitudes and current practices speaks from every page of this book – though its author, unlike *myself, dispenses with all polemic.*

Understandably, the demand for therapists who have faced up to their own fears, and are therefore competent to accompany the patient into even the most terrible experiences of his early life, is enormous. Up till now it has far outstripped supply. But in the foreseeable future the situation will be otherwise. The training of therapists has begun and in the meantime J. K. Stettbacher's book can help many readers use that preparatory period and encourage them not to give up hope of discovering their own truth. As this therapy offers scope for the free, creative application of one's own possibilities, it will almost certainly help many people make new discoveries – assuming, that is, that they are prepared to face the truth, whatever it may have in store for them.

The increasing application of Stettbacher's method will necessarily force medical practice to confront the truth of facts. It has been scientifically proved, for instance, that weeping caused by sadness, pain, and fear not only causes tears to fall. Stress hormones, which lead to a general relaxation of the body, are also released. Of course, this cannot be equated with therapy. Nevertheless, it is an important discovery that should find its way into the treatments used by therapeutic practitioners. So far, though, the opposite has been the case. Patients are given tranquilizers to calm them. What would happen if they began to gain access to the causes of their symptoms! The problem with medical pedagogy is that the majority of those involved, the institutions and specialists, in no way wish to know *why* it is people become ill. The result of this denial is that countless chronically ill people become permanent residents of our prisons and clinics, while billions are spent by the government on keeping mum about the truth. Those affected must on no account realize that they can be helped to understand the language of their childhood, thereby truly reducing their suffering or even relieving it altogether.

If we had the courage to confront the facts about the repression of childhood mistreatment and its consequences, this would be possible. One look at the specialist literature on the subject, however, shows just how lacking such courage is. By contrast, the literature is full of appeals to our good intention, all kinds of noncommittal and unverifiable advice, and, above all, moral preaching. Everything, all cruelty endured in childhood, is to be forgiven. If that doesn't do the trick, then the state must pay for the lifelong care and treatment of invalids and the chronically ill. But with the help of the truth, they could be cured.

It has now been proved that though repression may be crucial for a child, it should not necessarily be the fate of adults. A small child's dependency on its parents, its trust in them, its longing to love and be loved, are limitless. To exploit this dependency, to deceive a child in its longing, confuse it, and then proceed to sell this as "childrearing" is a criminal act – a criminal act committed hourly and daily out of ignorance, indifference, and the refusal to give up such behavior. The fact that the majority of such crimes are committed unconsciously does not, unfortunately, allay the calamitous consequences. The abused child's body will register the truth, while its consciousness refuses to acknowledge it. By repressing the pain and the accompanying situations, the infantile organism averts death – its fate, were it to consciously experience such traumatization.

What remains is the vicious circle of repression: the true story, which has been suppressed in the body, produces symptoms so that it could at last be recognized and taken seriously. But our consciousness refuses to comply, just as it did in childhood – because it was *then* that it learned the life-saving function of repression, and because no one has subsequently explained that as grown-ups we are not condemned to die of our knowledge, that, on the contrary, such knowledge would help us in our quest for health.

The dangerous teaching of "poisonous pedagogy" – "Thou Shalt Not Be Aware Of What Was Done To You" – reappears in the methods of treatment practiced by doctors, psychiatrists, and therapists. With medication and mystifying theories they try to influence their patients' memories as deeply as possible, in order that they never find the cause of their illness. These lie, almost without exception, in the psychic and physical mistreatment and neglect suffered in childhood.

Today, we know that AIDS and cancer involve a drastic collapse of the body's immune system, and that this physical "resignation" precedes the sick person's loss of hope. Incredibly, hardly anyone has taken the step that these discoveries suggest: that we can regain our hope, if our distress signals are finally heard. If our repressed, hidden story is at last perceived with full consciousness, even our immune system can regenerate itself. But who is there to help, when all the "helpers" fear their own personal history? And so we play the game of blindman's buff with each other – patients, doctors, medical authorities – because until now only a few people have experienced the fact that emotional access to the truth is the *indispensable precondition* of healing. In the long run, we can only function with consciousness of the truth. This also holds for our physical well-being. Bogus traditional morality, destructive religious interpretations, and confusion in our methods of childrearing all make this experience harder and hinder our initiative. Without a doubt, the pharmaceutical industry also profits from our blindness and despondency. However, each of us has been given only one life and only one body. It refuses to be fooled, insisting with all means at its disposal that we do not deceive it.

If, one day, the secret of childhood were to become no longer a secret, the state would be able to save the immense sums that it spends on hospitals, psychiatric clinics, and prisons maintaining our blindness. That this might deliberately happen is almost too incredible a thought. The money could be spent helping people relieve the repression that makes them ill, to help them recognize what happened to them in childhood and to resolve its consequences, so that they might live a responsible, conscious life. People who *know and feel* what happened to them in their childhood will never want to harm others. They will protect life and not wish to destroy it, for that is our biological purpose.

Sadly, there is little to be proud of in our tradition of child torture and child murder. It is to be thanked for our cynicism and indifference to the suffering of children. Using different examples, this is what I have tried to show in this book – that tradition is also to be thanked for our blindness to the fact that we are in the process of destroying the generations to come, and ultimately, life itself, with our cruelty sanctioned by tradition. It is therefore high time that we were brave enough to orient ourselves to the facts and to our own experience, rejecting that destructive inheritance, even though it may have, up to now, appeared in the best of lights.

Appendix B

Notes on Finding Assistance

For someone who wants outside help, there is a great deal available. There are many forms of help available but since psychologists are the most popular, this appendix centers on suggestions and cautions in finding a psychologist to work with.

If friends or family can't recommend someone, most counties have psychological associations which can refer you to a therapist.

Shopping for a therapist is like shopping for a used car. You might get lucky and like the first car you see but often you need to look at more than one.

Therapy has limitations and knowing those limitations can help avoid disappointment. Going to a therapist with the attitude, "I drink too much. It is your job to stop me" is a waste of time and money. A therapist can't do it for you.

Psychiatrists have entirely different training than psychologists. While there are competent and capable psychiatrists, they tend to look at problems in living as the result of "brain disease." It is much safer to go to a trusted psychologist and, if he recommends drug treatment, continue psychological treatment while seeing the psychiatrist for medication.

Asking for treatment for "alcoholism," a drinking problem or drug use is asking for a twelve step "therapist."

Going to an alcoholism or addiction "expert" is going to a grouper.

A therapist who believes in the twelve steps finds nothing unethical in spending months establishing trust in order to convince a client of his powerlessness and his need for "a support group." They are following a higher authority than their profession. They are following "God" as revealed through twelve step scripture.

One of the most popular tricks used by groupers is giving a test to determine if you are alcoholic. AA literature suggests telling someone, "Why don't you just try to drink moderately for three months and then you'll know." The key word is "try." A hypnotherapist uses the word try, as in "the more you try to open your eyes the tighter they will lock shut." The word "try" implies failure. The hypnotherapist uses the word in this context to *suggest failure.*

There are also written tests which pick up on bad reasons for drinking, frequency of over-consumption and severity of over-consumption. The purpose of the test is to identify someone with a "progressive, incurable disease" characterized by "denial."

Any effort on the part of a therapist to prove "alcoholism" is a clear signal to immediately terminate the relationship and find a new therapist.

Words used by the therapist can be keys to their twelve step status. Among these are "codependency" "inner child," "sobriety" and "recovery."

A suggestion to attend just one meeting to see if you like it or to see what AA is really like is grounds for immediately terminating the relationship. The most powerful influence in cult indoctrination is making someone a "minority of one." Among those most easily influenced in this situation are those who believe they won't be influenced.

Use of the word "spiritual" is also a danger signal. While not all who use the word are groupers, many religions, particularly New Age groups, do not consider themselves religious and hold their religious views as "universal truths" above and beyond other religions. If someone is advertising "spiritual" therapy make sure their religion is yours.

Once you find a suitable therapist, one you have confidence in, are able to establish a rapport with *and who has confidence in your ability to moderate or abstain*, it is time to take gambles with openness. While there are many types of therapy, the keys to success are the same as if you're not in therapy. This is learning to be more honest and open and developing the courage to look within oneself *deeply enough to like what you see.*

For those who feel a need for a group, there is a new, psychologically oriented organization called Rational Recovery (RR). As of September 1992, abstinence-oriented RR had meetings in 500 cities and also inpatient hospital treatment which uses their technique. RR can be especially recommended for those who have significant exposure to AA, since the core of their program strikes at the addiction promoting beliefs of personal powerlessness and incompetence. They do not promise being "catapulted into the fourth dimension of existence," but focus on the more reasonable, and successful, approach of pointing out where people make their decisions, making clear that one really has the power to make a choice. People are expected to deal with their problem and move on with their life. The meetings are free. The location of the nearest meeting can be found by writing Rational Recovery Self-Help Network, P.O. Box 800, Lotus, CA 95651 or calling (916) 621-4374 or (916) 621-2667.

Appendix C

The Substance Abuse Proclivity Profile (SAP)

The SAP is an excellent example of the use of an extremely useful tool, the MMPI, to "prove" AA doctrine and gain acceptability for AA language. The SAP successfully discriminates between young male substance abusers, putative normals and non-substance abusing psychiatric outpatients. It is useful for those between the ages of 13 and 26. Validity falls off rapidly afterward.

The scale is divided into three "factors:" "Extroversion," "Rebelliousness" and "Self-Pity." While there is room for criticism of designer MacAndrew's analysis of the first two factors, the third is most interesting.

AA doctrine asserts that the alcoholic is guilty of self-pity. The SAP scale proves it. Substance abusers score high on "Self-Pity." A look at the 10 questions which make up the self-pity factor, however, shows more ideology (or perhaps theology) than "Self-Pity."

My Webster's defines self-pity as "pity for oneself." It defines pity as "sympathy with the grief or misery of another." The dictionary definition does not discriminate what we may find "distasteful" or "pathological" from what is expected and considered "normal and natural."

What MacAndrew means is related to a distastful or pathological "pity for oneself." This is made clear in his statement, "Since it is Self-Pity that unifies this 'litany of lamentations,' that is how I have labeled this factor."

Three of the self-pity factor questions deal with vague fears.

> #543: Several times a week I feel as if something dreadful is about to happen.
> #494: I am afraid of finding myself in a closet or small closed place.
> #365: I feel uneasy indoors.

Substance abusers are more likely to answer "True" to the three questions. MacAndrew holds this as the substance abusers inclination to "portray themselves as victims."

If young substance abusers have these vague fears in disproportion to other groups, which apparently they do, they have two choices when *asked* if they do. They can either tell the truth and prove "self-pity" by marking these questions "True" or they can prove another doctrinal point about alcoholics. They can lie.

> #202: I believe I am a condemned person.
> #484: I have one or more faults which are so big that it seems better to accept them and try to control them rather than to try to get rid of them.

MacAndrew holds the tendency to respond "True" to these as again "portray[ing] themselves as victims." It seems much more accurate under the situation of taking the MMPI that they were merely expressing honest beliefs about themselves based in learned helplessness. There are also other possibilities. The sample is *in treatment* where they are being pressured to admit "I am powerless over alcohol." They are constantly being pressured to admit the flaws which prove their disease. They are also learning they can't change these faults and must wait until Step Seven, "Humbly asked God to remove our shortcomings," for the program to change them. Rather than "self-pity," perhaps this is a sign of treatment success.

Since those who abuse alcohol and drugs more often come from disordered homes and have a higher frequency of one or both parents being alcohol or drug abusers, "accurate estimation of circumstances" may well be a better interpretation of the "True" response given by young substance abusers to the following questions.

> #157: I feel that I have often been punished without cause.
>
> #338: I have certainly had more than my share of things to worry about.

It would seem that just *being in treatment for substance abuse* is more than most people have to worry about. To state such *when asked* is hardly part of a "litany of lamentations."

Answering "True" to the remaining three questions can be viewed as evidence of "self-pity." They can also, however, be seen as the result of growing up (or being half grown up) in a family in which there was intense competition between siblings for limited parental attention, approval and affection.

> #469: I have often found people jealous of my good ideas, just because they had not thought of them first.
>
> #331: If people had not had it in for me I would have been much more successful.

#507: I have frequently worked under people who seem to have things arranged so that they get credit for good work but are able to pass off mistakes onto those under them.

MacAndrew sums up the information provided by the SAP scale,

"From a remedial perspective it would seem, ... that when this sort of mordant self-absorption is detected, 'treatment' might profitably focus upon its radical transformation."

No doubt many young substance abusers would benefit from therapy in which they learned to clearly recognize their fears and put them in a proper perspective. Anything which counteracted their pervasive sense of helplessness, their lack of self-efficacy, would be helpful. They would benefit from support for their *rightness* in a *wrong* environment. They could learn that whatever jealousy and competition exists in their home environment is far from universal and that as they grow up they have increasing power to choose their associates.

MacAndrews analysis leads to a diagnosis of substance abuse with a definition of the substance abuser as more or less a self-pitying wretch. This logically leads to "treatment" for learned helplessness which begins with confessing "I am powerless" and to "treatment" for vague fears which is learning that fear is "an evil and corroding thread." Success at suppressing fear would make the young substance abuser more like his adult addict and alcoholic counterparts. He would be more likely to respond "True" to the MMPI's "Evil spirits possess me at times."

Young male substance abusers do differ from the

"putative normal" college student. It is questionable how much they differ from the average young person. The "Self-Pity Factor" shows they are having difficulties growing up but longitudinal studies show they do grow up. That is, of course, unless they get what MacAndrew himself needed to use quotes for, "treatment."

Regardless of how high young substance abusers score on the Self-Pity Factor, "self-pity" is a gross misnomer of scant value as diagnosis or as a guide in treatment. The grouping of these questions under the title "Self-Pity Factor" only serves to lend an air of respectability to AA doctrine and give respectability to AA language.

Appendix D

Further Reading

Alcoholism and Addiction
Herbert Fingarette
> In *Heavy Drinking: The Myth of Alcoholism as a Disease*, philosopher and former consultant to the World Health Organization on alcoholism Fingarette is simple, direct and to the point. University of California Press, Berkeley:1988

Stanton Peele
> *The Meaning of Addiction: Compulsive Experience and Its Interpretation* is the most comprehensive work on addiction available. Social psychologist Peele gives a detailed and thoroughly documented account of the broadest range of addictions. Lexington Books, Lexington, Massachusetts:1985.
>
> Also by Mr. Peele, *Diseasing of America: Addiction Treatment Out of Control*, Lexington Books, Lexington, Massachusetts:1989 and *The Truth About Addiction and Recovery* (and Archie Brodsky with Mary Arnold), Simon and Schuster, New York:1991

Cults/Totalitarian Groups/Indoctrination
Robert J Lifton
> *Thought Reform and the Psychology of Totalism: A*

Study of "Brainwashing" in China is the classic work on thought reform and totalitarianism. First published in 1961, this book has become more relevant with time. It has been used by both those founding totalitarian groups and those working to understand them. The techniques used and the environment and internal experiences of those who escaped the Chinese Communists are familiar to all who have a brush with modern American cults. University of North Carolina Press, Chapel Hill, 1989

Edgar Schein (with Inge Schneier and Curtis H. Barker)
Coercive Persuasion: A Socio-psychological Analysis of the "Brainwashing" of American Civilian Prisoners by the Chinese Communists, W. W. Norton & Company, New York:1961

Steve Hassan
In writing of groups he describes as "destructive cults," Steve Hassan builds on his experience as a Moonie. The groups he writes about are predominately communal cults. The methods used by these groups are more sophisticated than those of the Chinese Communists and more directly parallel twelve step "treatment." Also covered in detail is how to assist someone involved in a cult. *Combatting Cult Mind Control*, Park Street Press, Rochester, VT.:1988

Stanley Milgram
Obedience to Authority: An Experimental View, Harper & Row, New York:1969

Solomon E. Ashe
Studies of Independence and Conformity: I. A Minority of One Against a Unanimous Majority, *Psychological Monographs: General and Applied*, 70(1956):1-70

Peter T. Furst
Hallucinogens and Culture. Although the discussion centers around the use of hallucinogens in primitive religion, it lends a context for understanding the

Oxford Group conversion techniques and the 1950s use of LSD (until outlawed) by Bill Wilson and others for "spiritual experiences" for both himself and hospitalized patients. Chandler & Sharp, Novato, California: 1976

The Oxford Group
H. A. Walter
Soul-Surgery is the instruction manual for practicing Oxford Group's 5 C's. The Oxford Group, Oxford:1932
A. J. Russell
For Sinners Only was Oxford Group's "Big Book." Extremely tame in comparison to much of their other literature, its primary purpose was to attract new members. Hodder and Stoughton, London:1937
Marjorie Harrison
Saints Run Mad is an analysis of the Oxford Group from a Christian perspective. Harrison's observations about the group and the doctrine still reads amazingly well more than 50 years later as a criticism of present-day groupers. John Lane the Bodley Head Ltd., London:1934
Tom Driberg
In *The Mystery of Moral Re-Armament: A Study of Frank Buchman and His Movement*, Tom Driberg traces Frank Buchman and his movement from the earliest days to the 1960s. The pro-Nazi sympathies of the movement and political association with some of this centuries worst despots is discussed. Secker & Warburg, London: 1964

Psychiatry
While the bulk of the recommended reading is written by psychiatrists, these are all particularly outstanding people in the field. The following works by Thomas Szasz and *Thou Shalt Not Be Aware* by Alice Miller in "The

Self" category offer blistering criticism of vast segments of the profession. With all due respect to the remarkable people in the field, I must state that I do not hold a member of the profession with one of the highest suicide rates as particularly competent to help others with emotional issues by virtue of that membership. Traditional psychoanalysis has lost its credibility but, unfortunately, the ideas that have supplanted it are no better.

> Patient to psychiatrist, "I have been really sad this week."
> Psychiatrist, "Let's try a change in your medication and see if that helps."

Thomas S. Szasz

> *The Manufacture of Madness: A Comparative Study of the Inquisition and the Mental Health Movement.* The comparison is chillingly detailed and documented. Harper & Row, New York:1977
> In *The Myth of Mental Illness: Foundations of a Theory of Personal Conduct* noted psychiatrist Szasz debunks the dogma of "brain disease" as an explanation for socially unacceptable behavior. Harper & Row, New York:1974

The Self

The following authors present different perspectives on "the self." While there is great divergence in their views and the models used, all are removed from the "because I (you) are 'bad/sinful/sick'" as an indepth explanation of personality and behavior. Rather than being a list of books to help someone find out what is wrong with them, either directly or indirectly, they can be used to find one's inner strength and wisdom.

Alice Miller

Alice Miller's *Thou Shalt not be Aware: Society's Betrayal of the Child*, notes many of her discoveries in her years as a psychoanalyst. One of the most important points is that when people come to terms with childhood trauma they get well remarkably fast and don't need decades on the couch. Especially recommended for those who have had limited or no success with therapy. This book is difficult to categorize because not only is it a classic criticism of psychoanalysis but serves equally as well in providing the necessary information and intellectual framework to be able to recognize, and overcome, one's own internal barriers to awareness, independence and competence. Penguin, New York:1986

For Your Own Good: Hidden Cruelty in Child-Rearing and the Roots of Violence clearly documents the damage done, not only to individuals, but to society at large by *commonly accepted* methods of child rearing. Using the three main examples of Adolf Hitler, a child-murderer and a drug addict, Alice Miller makes the origins of their behavior and what *we* must do to stop *making* destructive and self-destructive people abundantly clear.

Martin E. P. Seligman

Helplessness: On Depression, Development, and Death is a detailed account of research on learned helplessness. W. H. Freeman and Company, New York:1975

Nathaniel Brandon

If only one book is to be read in this category, *The Disowned Self* is a must. Bantam, New York:1973

How to Raise Your Self-Esteem is a "do it yourself" book. Mr. Brandon's concept of self-esteem is far removed from today's "self-esteem movement." He does not suggest standing in front of a mirror trying to convince oneself, "I am handsome," "I have a relationship" or "I am tall." His concept of self-esteem has to do with learning the value of what is real within oneself. Bantam, New York:1987

Alexander Lowen

The title *Narcissism: Denial of the True Self* is misleading. When we think of Narcissism, we think of someone who is obsessed with his good looks. Remember, Narcissus was so taken by his *image* in a pool of water that he starved to death looking at it. He obviously wasn't a pretty sight as he approached starvation. The reflected image, not his own substance, was what was important. In Lowen's model of Narcissism, "good" images share the stage with "bad" images. Excellent in delineating what is image and and what is substance. The development and price paid for the valuation of image over substance is detailed. MacMillan, New York:1985

Also by Alexander Lowen is *The Betrayal of the Body*, MacMillan, New York:1967

Edgar A. Barnett

Unlock Your Mind and be Free: A Practical Approach to Hypnotherapy presents a positive approach to recognizing and resolving internal conflicts. Westwood Publishing, Glendale, California:1979

Analytical Hypnotherapy details Barnett's approach to therapy and hypnotherapy. Westwood Publishing, Glendale, California.

Eric Berne

Eric Berne is the founder of Transactional Analysis, the most popular school of pop psychology of the 1970s. Berne intended to break down barriers between therapist and client by developing a language of therapy that facilitated communication and replace the language therapists used to talk about clients among themselves. Many forms of therapy in use today are based upon the TA concept of three main ego states, parent, child and adult. Codependents Anonymous, blending the language of psychology with twelve step doctrine, acknowledges two of them, parent and child. The "adult" ego state is not acknowledged; the individual must look to the group and elder authority.

Games People Play: The Psychology of Human Relationships, Ballantine Books, New York:1973

Claude Steiner

Games Alcoholics Play looks at alcoholism from the TA perspective. Ballantine Books, 1974

Frederick Perles

(Ralph F. Hefferline and Paul Goodman), *Gestalt Therapy: Excitement and Growth in the Human Personality* is in at least its 25th printing. The exercises presented, particularly the first few, are excellent for increasing one's awareness of emotions and feelings. This not only directly counteracts cult indoctrination but also opens the door to understanding many of the earlier influences which left one vulnerable to addiction and mind-control techniques in the first place. Highly recommended. Dell, New York:1951

Notes

1. Horace, book I, Ep. VI, cited from Harrison (1934)
2. AA (1957):174-175
3. AA (1984):209-210
4. Buchman (1961):xvii
5. Driberg (1964):52
6. Buchman (1961):24-25
7. Driberg (1964):193
8. MacMillan (1933):139-151
9. Walter (1932)
10. Walter (1932):30
11. Walter (1932):38
12. Walter (1932):33
13. Walter (1932):30
14. 'Ten Suggestions for Personal Work' cited from Walter (1932):44
15. Walter (1932):42
16. Walter (1932):61
17. Walter (1932):59
18. Walter (1932):52
19. Driberg (1964):62
20. Walter (1932):64
21. Walter (1932):64-78
22. MacMillan (1933):24
23. Walter (1932):92
24. Walter (1932):93
25. Walter (1932):18
26. Lean (1985):151-152
27. AA (1984):108
28. AA (1984):106
29. AA (1984):106
30. AA (1984):111
31. AA (1984):111
32. AA (1984):115
33. AA (1984):118
34. Pittman (1988):164
35. AA (1984):120
36. AA (1984):127
37. AA (1938):15
38. Lean (1985):152
39. AA (1957):68
40. AA (1984):136
41. AA (1980):68
42. AA (1984):146
43. AA (1957):74-75
44. AA (1980):140
45. AA (1980):158
46. AA (1984):174
47. AA (1984):174
48. AA (1984):174
49. AA (1984):174
50. AA (1984):174
51. AA (1984):190
52. AA (1984):198
53. AA (1957):viii
54. AA (1980):162
55. AA (1980):168
56. Birnie (1936)
57. AA (1957):96
58. AA (1976):xxii(f)
59. Alexander J, *Saturday Evening Post*, March 1, 1941, cited from AA reprint, The Jack Alexander Article...about A.A.
60. Minogue (1948)
61. Ditman et al (1967)
62. Brandesma, Maultsby and Welsh (1980)
63. Vaillant (1983a):283-285
64. Peele (1989):194
65. Vaillant (1983a):292
66. Vaillant (1983a):198
67. Vaillant (1983a):303
68. Vaillant (1983b)
69. White and Porter (1966)
70. AA (1987)
71. Levine (1978)
72. Peele (1989):54
73. Szasz (1977):154
74. Jellinek (1946)
75. Jellinek (1946):6-7
76. AA (1938):40

77. AA (1938):60
78. AA (1938):30
79. AA (1938):60
80. AA (1938):32-33
81. AA (1938):33
82. AA (1938):30
83. Edwards et al (1977)
84. Marlatt et al (1973)
85. Bigelow and Liebson (1972)
87. Davies (1962)
88. Maidman (1963)
89. Kjølstad (1963)
90. Polich (1980). see also Armor et al (1978) and Polich et al (1981)
91. Fillmore (1975)
92. Temple and Fillmore (1986)
93. Szasz (1977)
94. Rohan (1978)
95. Bennett et al (1982)
96. Robbins et al (1974)
97. Light and Torrance (1929)
98. Zinberg and Robertson (1972)
99. Wray and Dickerson (1981)
100. Hadaway (1979)
101. Falk (1981) and Falk and Tang (1980)
102. Seligman (1975)
103. Rozin, Poritsky and Sotsky (1971) cited from Seligman (1975)
104. Dembo, Dertke et al (1988) and Dembo, Williams et al (1988)
105. Nissan and Sandoval, Journal of Psychology and Human Sexuality
106. Tarter (1988):189
107. Tarter (1988):193
108. Schweitzer and Lawton (1989)
109. Emmelkamp (1988)
110. Jurich et al (1985)
111. Tarter (1988):191
112. Aronson and Gilbert (1963)
113. Tarter (1988):191
114. Tarter (1988):192
115. Tarter (1988):192
116. Tarter (1988):191
117. MacAndrew (1965)
118. AA (1976):171-172
119. AA (1980):10
120. AA (1980):10
121. Suzanne Windows, Bob Smith's daughter in AA (1980):10
122. AA (1980):12
123. AA (1980):12
124. AA (1976):172
125. AA (1984):14
126. AA (1984):15
127. AA (1984):24
128. AA (1984):20
129. AA (1984):22
130. AA (1984):24
131. AA (1984):24
132. AA (1984):25
133. AA (1984):25
134. AA (1984):27
135. AA (1984):36
136. AA (1984):37
137. Marshall (1979)
138. Ludwig and Lyle (1964)
139. Briddell (1978)
140. Lang et al (1981)
141. Lang, Goeckner and Adesso (1975)
142. Gray (1978)
143. Steele and Josephs (1988)
144. Russell and Bond (1980)
145. Jones and Berglas (1978)
146. Marlatt et al (1975)
147. Higgins and Marlatt (1975)
148. Donovan and Marlatt (1980)
149. Polich (1980):102
150. Schaeffer (1971)
151. Sanchez-Craig (1980), Sanchez-Craig et al (1984), and Sanchez-Craig and Lei (1986)
152. AA (1938):58-60
153. AA (1938):67-68
154. AA (1938):93
155. Asch (1956)

156. Lifton (1961):429
157. AA (1938):123
158. AA (1957):119
159. AA (1938):83-84
160. AA (1952):15
161. AA (1984):293
162. AA (1984):293
163. AA (1984):293
164. AA (1984):293-294
165. AA (1957):13
166. AA (1952):23
167. AA (1952):24
168. AA (1952):33
169. AA (1952):33
170. AA (1938):23
171. AA (1938):44
172. AA (1952):27
173. AA (1952):32
174. AA (1952):33
175. Birnie (1936)
176. AA (1952):34
177. AA (1952):35
178. AA (1952):36
179. AA (1952):36
180. AA (1952):36
181. AA (1952):37
182. AA (1952):41
183. AA (1938):63
184. AA (1938):75
185. AA (1952):62
186. AA (1952):62
187. AA (1938):62
188. AA (1938):64
189. AA (1938):66
190. AA (1938):67
191. AA (1952):48
192. AA (1938):68
193. AA (1938):67
194. AA (1952):60
195. AA (1952):60
196. AA (1938):74
197. AA (1952):61
198. AA (1952):60
199. AA (1952):60
200. AA (1952):60
201. AA (1952):65
202. AA (1952):66

203. AA (1952):67
204. AA (1952):69
205. AA (1952):69
206. AA (1952):69
207. AA (1938):76
208. AA (1952):74
209. AA (1952):70
210. AA (1952):72
211. AA (1952):75
212. AA (1952):100
213. Lifton (1961):427
214. Dukakis (1990):41
215. Dukakis (1990):23
216. Dukakis (1990):42
217. Dukakis (1990):78
218. Dukakis (1990):78
219. Dukakis (1990):107
220. Dukakis (1990):243
221. Dukakis (1990):86
222. Dukakis (1990):97
223. Dukakis (1990):101
224. Dukakis (1990):140
225. Dukakis (1990):13
226. Dukakis (1990):249
227. AA (1938):89
228. AA (1982)
229. AA (1984):283-285
230. AA (1952):129
231. Nace (1987):148
232. Nace (1987):60
233. Nace (1987):124
234. Nace (1987):xix
235. Nace (1987):xiv
236. Nace (1987):xiv
237. Ditman et al (1967) and
     Brandesma et al (1980)
238. AA (1976):245
239. cited from "Are we a nation
     of `addicts'?" *Long Beach
     Press- Telegram*, Sun Nov.
     18th, 1990
240. Lifton (1956)
241. *Sober Times*, Sept. 1990, p.
     29
242. Marlatt and Gordon (1980)
243. AA (1978):272
244. Szasz (1977):141

Sources

AA 1982, *AA as a Resource for the Medical Professional*. New York: Alcoholics Anonymous World Services, Inc.

AA 1938, *Alcoholics Anonymous*. New York: Works Publishing

AA 1952, *Twelve Steps and Twelve Traditions*. New York: Alcoholics Anonymous World Services, Inc.

AA 1957, *Alcoholics Anonymous Comes of Age*. New York: Alcoholics Anonymous World Services, Inc.

AA 1976, *Alcoholics Anonymous*. New York: Alcoholics Anonymous World Services, Inc.

AA 1980, *Dr. Bob and the Good Oldtimers*. New York: Alcoholics Anonymous World Services, Inc.

AA 1984, *Pass It On*. New York: Alcoholics Anonymous World Services, Inc.

AA 1987, *AA Membership Survey*. Alcoholics Anonymous World Services

Armor DJ, Polich JM, and Stambul HB, *Alcoholism and Treatment* (The Rand Reports two-year follow-up). New York: Wiley, 1978

Aronson H, and Gilbert A, Preadolescent Sons of Male Alcoholics. *Archives of General Psychiatry* 8(1963):235-241. Cited from Tartar (1988)

Asch SE, Studies of Independence and Conformity: I. A Minority of One Against a Unanimous Majority. *Psychological Monographs: General and Applied* 70(1956):1-70

Bennett R, Batenhorst R, Graves D, Foster TS, Baumann T, Griffen WO, and Wright BD, Morphine Titration in Postoperative Laparotomy Patients Using Patient-Controlled Analgesia. *Current Therapeutic Research* 32(1982):45-52

Bigelow G, Liebson I, Cost Factors Controlling Alcoholic Drinking, *The Psychological Record*, 22(1972):305-314

Birnie WAH, Hitler or Any Fascist Leader Controlled by God Could Cure All Ills of World, Buchman Believes. *New York World-Telegram*, Aug 26(1936). cited from Thornton-Duesbury (1964):130-133

Brandesma JM, Maultsby MC, and Welsh RJ, *The Outpatient Treatment of Alcoholism: A Review and Comparative Study.* Baltimore: University Park Press,1980

Briddell DW, Rimm DC, Caddy GR, Krawitz G, Sholis D, and Wunderlin RJ, Effects of Alcohol and Cognitive Set on Sexual Arousal to Deviant Stimuli. *Journal of Abnormal Psychology* 87(1978):418-430

Buchman F, *Remaking the World.* London: Blandford Press, 1961

Cohen M, Liebson IA, Faillace LA, and Allen RP, Moderate Drinking by Chronic Alcoholics: A Schedule-Dependent Phenomenon, *The Journal of Nervous and Mental Disease*, 153(1971):434-443

Davies MA, Normal Drinking in Recovered Alcohol Addicts. *Quarterly Journal of Studies on Alcohol* 23(1962):94-104

Dembo R, Dertke M, Borders S, Washburn M, and Schmeidler J, The Relationship Between Physical and Sexual Abuse and Tobacco, Alcohol, and Illicit Drug Use Among Youths in a Juvenile Detention Center. *The International Journal of the Addictions* 23(1988):351-378

Dembo R, Williams L, Wish ED, Dertke M, Berry E, Getreu A, Washburn M, and Schmeidler J, The Relationship between Physical and Sexual Abuse and Illicit Drug Use: A Replication among a New Sample of Youths Entering a Juvenile Detention Center. *The International Journal of the Addictions* 23(1988):1101-1123

Ditman KS, Crawford GG, Forgy EW, Moskowitz H, and MacAndrew C, A Controlled Experiment on the Use of Court Probation for Drunk Arrests. *American Journal of Psychiatry* 124(1967):160-163·

Donovan DM, and Marlatt GA, Assessment of Expectancies and Behaviors Associated with Alcohol Consumption: A Cognitive-Behavioral Approach. *Journal of Studies on Alcohol* 41(1980):1153-85

Driberg T, *The Mystery of Moral Re-Armament: A Study of Frank Buchman and His Movement*. London: Secker & Warburg, 1964

Dukakis K, and Scovell J, *Now You Know*. New York: Simon and Schuster, 1990

Edwards G, Orford J, Egert S, Guthrie S, Hawker A, Hensman C, Mitcheson M, Oppenheimer E, and Taylor C, Alcoholism: A Controlled Trial of "Treatment" and "Advice." *Journal of Studies on Alcohol* 38(1977):1004-1031

Emmelkamp PMG, Drug Addiction and Parental Rearing Style: A Controlled Study. *The International Journal of the Addictions* 23(1988):207-216

Falk JL, and Tang M, Schedule Induction and Overindulgence. *Alcoholism: Clinical and Experimental Research* 4(1980):266-270

Falk JL, The Environmental Generation of Excessive Behavior. In *Behavior in Excess*, S.J. Mulé, editor, pp. 313-337. New York: Free Press, 1981

Fillmore KM, Relationships between Specific Drinking Problems in Early Adulthood and Middle Age: An Exploratory 20-Year Follow-up Study. *Journal of Studies on Alcohol* 36(1975):882-907

Gray JA, Anxiety. *Human Nature* July(1978):38-45

Gustafson R, Self-Reported Expected Emotional Changes as a Function of Alcohol Intoxication by Alcoholic Men and Women. *Psychological Reports* 65(1989):67-74

Hadaway PF, Alexander BK, Coambs RB, and Beyerstein B, The Effect of Housing and Gender on Preference for Morphine- Sucrose Solutions in Rats. *Psychopharmacology* 66(1979):87-91

Harrison M, *Saints Run Mad*. John Lane the Bodley Head Ltd., London:1934

Higgins RL, and Marlatt GA, Fear of Interpersonal Evaluation as a Determinant of Alcohol Consumption in Male Social Drinkers. *Journal of Abnormal Psychology* 84(1975):644-651

Jellinek EM, Phases in the Drinking History of Alcoholics: Analysis of a Survey Conducted by the Official Organ of

Alcoholics Anonymous. *Quarterly Journal of Studies on Alcohol* 7(1946):1-88

Jones EE, and Berglas S, Control of Attributions about the Self Through Self-handicapping Strategies: The Appeal of Alcohol and the Role of Underachievement. *Personality and Social Psychology Bulletin* 4(1978):200-206

Jurich AP, Polson CJ, Jurich JA, and Bates RA, Family Factors in the Lives of Drug Users and Abusers. *Adolescence* 20(1985):143-159

Kjølstad T, Notes and Comment: Normal Drinking in Recovered Alcohol Addicts. *Quarterly Journal of Studies on Alcohol* 24(1963):730

Lang AR, Goeckner DJ, and Adesso VJ, Effects of Alcohol on Aggression in Male Social Drinkers. *Journal of Abnormal Psychology* 84(1975):508-518

Lang AR, Searles J, Lauerman R, and Adesso V, Expectancy, Alcohol and Sex Guilt as Determinants of Interest in and Reaction to Sexual Stimuli. *Journal of Abnormal Psychology* cited from Wilson (1981)

Lean G, *Frank Buchman: A Life.* London: Constable, 1985

Levine HG, The Discovery of Addiction: Changing Conceptions of Habitual Drunkenness in America. *Journal of Studies on Alcohol* 39(1978):143-174

Lifton RJ, "Thought Reform" of Western Civilians in Chinese Communist Prisons. *Psychiatry* 19(1956):173-195

Lifton RJ, *Thought Reform and the Psychology of Totalism: A Study of "Brainwashing" in China.* Chapel Hill and London: The University of North Carolina Press, 1961

Light AB, and Torrance EG, Opiate Addiction VI: The Effects of Abrupt Withdrawal Followed by Readministration of Morphine in Human Addicts, with Special Reference to the Composition of the Blood, the Circulation and the Metabolism. *Archives of Internal Medicine* 44(1929):1-16. cited from Peele (1985)

Ludwig AM, and Lyle WH, The Experimental Production of Narcotic Drug Effects and Withdrawal Symptoms Through Hypnosis. *The International Journal of Clinical and Experimental Hypnosis* 12(1964):1-17

MacAndrew C, The Differentiation of Male Alcoholic

Outpatients from Nonalcoholic Psychiatric Outpatients by Means of the MMPI. *Journal of Studies on Alcohol* 26(1965):238-246

MacMillan E, *Seeking and Finding*. New York & London: Harper & Brothers, 1933

Maidman MM, Notes and Comment: Normal Drinking in Recovered Alcohol Addicts. *Quarterly Journal of Studies on Alcohol* 24(1963):733-735

Marlatt GA, Demming B, and Reid JB, Loss of Control Drinking in Alcoholics: An Experimental Analogue. *Journal of Abnormal Psychology* 81(1973):233-241

Marlatt GA, Kosturn CF, and Lang AR, Provocation to Anger and Opportunity for Retaliation as Determinants of Alcohol Consumption in Social Drinkers. *Journal of Abnormal Psychology* 84(1975):652-659

Marlatt GA, and Gordon JR, Determinants of Relapse: Implications for the Maintenance of Behavior Change. in *Behavioral Medicine: Changing Health Lifestyles*, pp. 410-452, New York: Brunner/Mazel, 1980

Marshal M, *Weekend Warriors*, Palo Alto, Ca.: Mayfield, 1979. cited from Marlatt GA, Alcohol, the Magic Elixir: Stress, Expectancy, and the Transformation of Emotional States, in *Stress and Addiction*, vol. 3, p. 302-322

Minogue SJ, 'Alcoholics Anonymous.' *The Medical Journal of Australia* May 8(1948):586-587

Nace EP, *The Treatment of Alcoholism*. New York: Brunner/Mazel, 1987

Peele S, *The Meaning of Addiction: Compulsive Experience and Its Interpretation*. Lexington, Mass.: Lexington Books, 1985

Peele S, *The Diseasing of America: Addiction Treatment Out of Control*. Lexington, Mass.: Lexington Books, 1989

Pittman B, *AA: The Way it Began*. Seattle: Glen Abbey Books, 1988

Polich JM, Patterns of Remission in Alcoholism, pp. 95-112. In *Alcoholism Treatment in Transition*. Edwards SG, and Grant M, editors. London: Croom Helm, 1980

Polich JM, Armor DJ, and Braiker HB, *The Course of Alcoholism: Four Years After Treatment* (Rand Reports four year follow- up). New York: Wiley (1981)

Robins LN, Davis DJ, and Goodwin DW, Drug Use by U.S. Army Enlisted Men in Vietnam: A Follow-up on their Return Home. *American Journal of Epidemiology* 99(1974):235-249

Rohan WP, Comment on "The N.C.A. Criteria for the Diagnosis of Alcoholism; an Empirical Evaluation Study." *Journal of Studies on Alcohol* 39(1978)211-218

Rozin P, Poritsky S, and Stosky R, American Children with Reading Problems can Easily Learn to Read English Represented by Chinese Characters. *Science* 171(1971):1264- 1267

Russell JA, and Bond CR, Individual Differences in Beliefs Concerning Emotions Conducive to Alcohol Use. *Journal of Studies on Alcohol* 41(1980):753-759

Sanchez-Craig M, Random Assignment to Abstinence or Controlled Drinking in a Cognitive-Behavioral Program: Short-Term Effects on Drinking Behavior. *Addictive Behaviors* 5(1980):35-39

Sanchez-Craig M, Annis HM, Bornet AR, and MacDonald KR, Random Assignment to Abstinence and Controlled Drinking: Evaluation of a Cognitive-Behavioral Program for Problem Drinkers. *Journal of Consulting and Clinical Psychology* 52(1984):390- 403

Sanchez-Craig M, and Lei M, Disadvantages of Imposing the Goal of Abstinence on Problem Drinkers: an empirical study. *British Journal of Addiction* 81(1986):505-512

Schaeffer HH, A Cultural Delusion of Alcoholics. *Psychological Reports* 29(1971):587-589

Schweitzer RD, and Lawton PA, Drug Abusers' Perceptions of their Parents. *British Journal of Addiction* 84(1989):309-314

Seligman MEP, *Helplessness: On Depression, Development, and Death.* New York: W. H. Freeman and Company, 1975

Steele CM, and Josephs RA, Drinking Your Troubles Away II: An Attention-Allocation Model of Alcohol's Effect on Psychological Stress. *Journal of Abnormal Psychology* 97(1988):196-205

Stewart RM, and Brown RI, An Outcome Study of Gamblers Anonymous, *Br. J. of Psychiatry* 152(1988):284-288

Szasz TS, *The Manufacture of Madness*. New York: Harper & Row, 1977

Tarter RE, Are There Inherited Behavioral Traits That Predispose to Substance Abuse? *Journal of Consulting and Clinical Psychology* 56(1988):189-196

Temple MT, and Fillmore KM, The Variability of Drinking Patterns and Problems among Young Men, Age 16-31: A Longitudinal Study. *The International Journal of the Addictions* 20(1986):1595-1620

Thornton-Duesbery JP, *The Open Secret of MRA: An examination of Mr. Driberg's 'critical examination' of Moral Re-Armament*. London: Blandford Press, 1964

Vaillant GE, 1983a. *The Natural History of Alcoholism*. Cambridge, London: Harvard University Press, 1983

Vaillant GE, 1983b. Can Alcoholics Go Back to "Social" Drinking?. *Harvard Medical School Health Letter* Oct(1983):3-5

Walter HA, *Soul-Surgery*. Oxford: The Oxford Group, 1932

White FW, and Porter TL, Self Concept Reports among Hospitalized Alcoholics during Early Periods of Sobriety. *Journal of Counseling Psychology* 13(1966):352-355

Wilson GT, The Effects of Alcohol on Human Sexual Behavior. *Advances in Substance Abuse* 2(1981):3-40

Wray I, and Dickerson MG, Cessation of High Frequency Gambling and 'Withdrawal' Symptoms. *British Journal of Addiction* 76(1981):401-405

Zinberg NE, and Robertson JA, *Drugs and the Public*. New York: Simon & Schuster, 1972. Cited from Peele (1985)

COMMUNICATIONS

There are many questions and areas of concern I would have liked to address but the documentation was insufficient. Any information a reader is able to share would be greatly appreciated. Some of the unanswered questions include:

Oxford Group's founder was "working" in China as early as 1918. Did the Chinese communists learn their methods from the early groupers?

Rev. Shoemaker, the American head of the Oxford Group who presumably precipitated the break with Bill Wilson's group, later advised Bill Wilson to include the personal stories in the back of the Big Book. Did the Oxford Group and AA ever *really* split or just have a "lover's quarrel"? The AA corporation had a significant number of "non-alcoholics" on their board of directors until at least the 1950s. Were they Oxford Groupers? Who runs AA now?

How many of the early doctors and psychiatrists who praised AA in the scientific literature were Oxford Groupers? Dr. Harry M. Tiebout converted National Council on Alcoholism founder Marty Mann with the Big Book during a sixteen-month hospitalization. Were he and Bill Wilson's Dr. Silkworth Groupers?

What groups, like the National Council on Alcoholism, are front groups for twelve steppers? How deeply are AA members involved in national, state and local government? How are government funds being used, either directly or indirectly, to indoctrinate? According to Los Angeles magazine, two of the television networks have on-site meetings. How deeply is AA involved in the media?

Bill Wilson was involved in the use of LSD in the conversion of hospitalized patients in the 1950s. How deeply was AA involved?

There have been reports of people being confined against their will, and forced to undergo indoctrination. The ones I know of are currently under litigation. How frequently does this occur? What has been your experience?

There are other groups founded by former AA members which, although not associated with AA, use the same techniques. Who are these groups?

Moral Re-Armament (Oxford Group) was still around in the 1960s. What has become of them and their leaders? Did they undergo another name change or did they die out?

Stanton Peele reports problems for researchers whose work contradicts twelve step doctrine. For those who work with alcoholics, addicts, codependents, etc., do you know of any blacklisting, loss of grants, firings or any similar situation?

There is much written on the large number of suicides and attempted suicides among people who "qualify" for twelve step membership. There is, however, little documentation of their membership status and whether attempts disproportionately occur after exposure to the groupers. Are there any studies which compare the suicide rate among "disease victims" in the general population with comparable groups who are twelve steppers? Do any studies compare the suicide rate of those intimately involved with groupers with those who merely have the "unrecognized" disease? What is your experience?

There have been reports of successful litigation against Alcoholics Anonymous but little has reached the mass media. Do you know of any such lawsuits?

What has been your personal experience? Have you or a relative been adversely affected? Have you had a grouper for a therapist? What forms of therapy have you found most useful and most harmful? Did you stop alone? To what do you attribute your successes and your failures?

There is, as far as I know, no referral service that doesn't lead directly to the groups. A non-grouper referral service is much needed. Please send any suggestions you have on how this might be accomplished.

General comment and critical review is greatly appreciated.

Ken Ragge
c/o Alert! Publishing
P.O.Box 50233
Henderson, NV. 89016-0233

BOOKS BY ALICE MILLER

THE DRAMA OF THE GIFTED CHILD
(originally published as *Prisoners of Childhood,* also available as a Harper audio cassette)

FOR YOUR OWN GOOD: HIDDEN CRUELTY IN CHILD-REARING AND THE ROOTS OF VIOLENCE

THOU SHALT NOT BE AWARE: PSYCHOANALYSIS AND SOCIETY'S BETRAYAL OF THE CHILD

PICTURES OF A CHILDHOOD: SIXTY-SIX WATER-COLORS AND AN ESSAY

THE UNTOUCHED KEY: TRACING CHILDHOOD TRAUMA IN CREATIVITY AND DESTRUCTIVE-NESS

BANISHED KNOWLEDGE: FACING CHILDHOOD INJURIES

BREAKING DOWN THE WALL OF SILENCE: THE LIBERATING EXPERIENCE OF FACING PAINFUL TRUTH